The Vitamin D Lifestyle and Recipe Book
ISBN: 978-82-93680-00-0
© 2018 Vanessa Raphael Michel

For more info & resources visit:
vanessaraphael.com
vitamindlifestyle.com
outstandinghealth.fit
vitamindlifestylebook.com

Some texts written by Michael Cawley, as credited and used with his permission.
Testimonies written by the patients themselves, used with their permission.

All recipes cooked, enjoyed and photographed by Vanessa Raphael Michel and Tobias Michel.

Design: Tobias Michel, tobiasmichel.com
Body text set in Raleway Regular 10pt, Recipes in 14pt size for easy readability.
Other fonts: Raleway Bold, *Georgia Italic*, OCTIN STENCIL
Photos: Vanessa Raphael Michel and Tobias Michel
Except for: photo on cover (upper): Fernando-brasil-103271-unsplash
Photos on pages 4, 12, 23, 25, 26, 33, 34, 36, 41, 43, 44, 45, 46, 49, 50, 52, 62 (Himalaya), 112, 196, 199, 200, 201, 202, 205 (jogging), 207, 209: unsplash.com
Other photos as credited. All images used with permission.

Disclaimer:

The Vitamin D

Lifestyle and Recipe

Book

By

VANESSA RAPHAEL *MICHEL*

Thanks

First of all I want to give thanks to my Lord and Saviour, Jesus Christ, without Him I would not be here in the first place.

I want to give thanks to my husband Tobias who has been an amazing support these years of hardship with illness. Thank you for providing for us, taking care of me, making us food, cleaning the house and now also helping me making this book.

I want to thank our newfound church for offering prayers and support and showing love.

I want to especially thank Michael Cawley, my Coimbra Protocol Specialist for being available to me in a hard time and offering support through his amazing knowledge on how the body works with vitamin D3, magnesium and other helpful supplements. Thank you for always having an attitude of hope for the possibilities of a good outcome, and not giving up on your patients even when they have challenging days for them and for you.

I want to thank Dr Cicero Galli Coimbra for laying down his life for this treatment - high doses of vitamin D3 - and giving hope to so many people that without this protocol would have to succumb to big pharma drugs and their side effects as the only option to exist for a given time.

In memory of my beloved mother who is not among us anymore, but hopefully smiling down from Heaven as now other people with auto immune diseases have the chance to get the treatment she never got.

– Vanessa Raphael

Table of content

Continues on next page

Mind, Exercise & Creativity

Testimonies

VITAMIN D3 ESSENTIALS

«For a healthy person, I can say without a doubt that 10 000 iu of vitamin D a day will not pose any risk, quite the contrary. For those who suffer from any auto immune disease, this will provide partial relief, but will not eliminate the problem. Higher doses can be used, as long as this supplementation is done under medical supervision.»

Dr. Cicero G. Coimbra

About This Book and Clean Eating

On the Coimbra Protocol the vitamin D3 is an immunomodulator, so you don't need a strict diet that claims to heal MS etc. This recipe book will take a lot of stress away from people who already struggle with MS and auto immune diseases that have more challenges than eating a low calcium diet and the regular blood and calcium tests etc.

However if you already eat gluten-free and feel that is helping you, by all means continue with doing that. This book is about helping you eat calcium restricted in a clean and healthy way. When I say clean eating I am referring to foods that have had a life like swimming in the sea, running on free range farms or growing on the ground, having

eliminated high GI (glycemic index) foods such as white rice, pasta and white potatoes.

It also means no corn syrup, no GMO, no artificial sweeteners, no processed foods that have contents that you don't know how to pronounce because it was made in a laboratory.

That being said, there are a few high glycemic dishes included as not all people have the intention to follow a clean eating diet, but a calcium restricted diet.

There are also quite a few vegan friendly dishes as well as vegetarian friendly dishes. So all you have to do is remove the chicken

«Replenishing with vitamin D3 in the doses required to achieve its beneficial effects implies restoring a natural mechanism, which allow patients to resume a normal life. It's a mechanism that took nature millions of years to develop, and even if the pharmaceutical industry spent 400 years working on this issue, they would not get close to the benefits that vitamin D3 can provide to these patients».

Dr. Cicero Coimbra, Neurologist, PhD.
On the comparison between conventional drugs for auto immune diseases and Vitamin D3.

like in the Pad Thai dish and add eggs if you are vegetarian and not at all if you are vegan.

It has not been an overly easy task to put this together when taking into consideration almost everything people want.

But it is a recipe book that can help people starting on the Coimbra Protocol/taking higher doses of vitamin D3 to know what to eat. This book is a collection of healthy dishes I have eaten throughout the years and can be consumed by anyone who wants to learn to eat clean, - but also for those who understand it is necessary in order to realign their health.

Your genes will tell you what you are created to eat

To be absolutely sure of what foods your body can tolerate, a gene test can be taken, pinpointing food allergies and acceptable foods specific to your genes. It is called nutri genomics and I took one this summer that helped me cut through all the noise of all the diets that want to claim they are right for me. Foremost we have over 4000 vitamin D3 gene receptors in the body that need to be fed. And when they get fed the body comes into harmony.

About the Author

Vanessa Raphael is a multi passionate entrepreneur, vlogger/blogger, jewellery designer who has produced jewellery for high fashion photo shoots, events such as Miss World Norway, celebrities and a member of the Norwegian Royal Family.

She is also the creator and host of the Social Media for Health Preneurs Summit, founder of the course Instagram Integrity Marketing, Outstanding Health and Vitamin D Lifestyle. A Networker and Health Ambassador, Vanessa Raphael has a genuine gift for networking and connecting the dots of her passions in life with the right people.

Vanessa Raphael embarked on an intense health journey since the end of 2015. Leading up to recently discovering information about health as well as prayer that has been of great benefit for her. She started on the only protocol that halts MS and auto immune disorders by suppressing them with high doses of vitamin D3 under medical supervision.

She also found an invaluable gene test that helped her find out many things about her nutrigenomics; such as that she is not gluten intolerant nor caffeine sensitive for example. It has helped her to find what diet is best suited for her among the vast majority of diet fads, which all again pointed back to clean eating.

All these discoveries have been a God-send and she wishes that this information was more widespread, so that people in need can find other alternatives than Big Pharma lifelong prescriptions to expensive medical drugs which may or may not halt any diseases at all. When her mother died from progressive form for MS in 2013 it was clear to Vanessa Raphael that she had not received help for this illness as there was and still is no public endorsed information about alternative approaches that could send diseases into remission.

With this current journey fresh in memory, Vanessa Raphael wants to help patients and their doctors, nutritionist etc with this lifestyle and recipe book that is calcium restricted and clean eating based.

My Story

My mum and me sometimes in the 1980s

young. I personally suffered a lot of trauma observing the illness progression and helpless to do anything but pray. She used to ask me; "Have they found a cure yet?" as tears would run down from her eyes. It was heartbreaking to say the least.

Five years ago my mum died from MS. She had the most aggressive type of MS, Primary Progressive Multiple Sclerosis (PPMS), and became paralyzed from the mouth down. It started when she was a normal, healthy woman in her early forties. After a long time of suffering symptoms, she was diagnosed with MS, followed by a rapid progression of the illness.

Under supervision of severe knowledge deficient doctors trained solely by big pharmaceutical companies to drug down patients, like my mum, with their cruel drugs that did not halt the disease or the rapid illness progression, she died only 63 years

In the period before she died, I was also sick with a long time sinus infection, thyroid problems, and low vitamin D3 levels. My doctor said I could take 20 mcg of vitamin D3 but to be careful taking 40 mcg of vitamin D! With this ridiculous advice from a knowledge deficient doctor, I started to research for more information about vitamin D3. I found some groups on Facebook about the topic and that is also how I discovered the Coimbra Protocol. However, the information back then was limited and most of it was in Portuguese. At that time my mum was in the very late stages of her illness and could not travel from Norway to Brazil. Miraculously, I recovered enough to visit her in the hospital a couple times before she died and I later arranged her funeral.

About 3 years ago I became sicker than I was previously, constantly fatigued, eye problems such as cramps and flashing (photopsia), and just not feeling well overall. We tried to find out what it was. I increased my daily dose of vitamin D3 to 10,000iu a day but I still got worse. After several complaints to my doctor (another one), also reminding her that my mum had MS, I finally got an MRI. The MRI lab found some lesions in my brain and wrote in their report, «Cannot rule out the possibility of progressive demyelinating illness». However, my first examination with a neurologist resulted in, «No clinical signs of MS».

Two months after my first neurologist appointment, I felt pretty desperate about my declining condition, so I contacted a trained Coimbra Protocol Specialist who got me started on the Coimbra Protocol. However, when the dose of vitamin D3 was raised to 90,000 iu, I felt very unpleasant. I got an unbearable

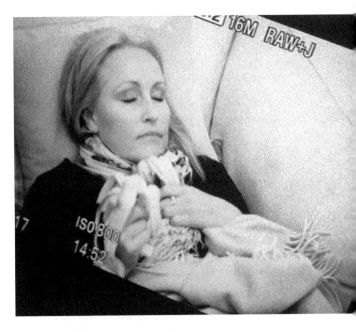

Life with fatigue 2013-2018:
I got dressed up and all fixed up to go to my best friend's hen party but got too fatigued and had to cancel. Got exhausted while I was eating a banana.

My mum at her 50th birthday in 2000

tinnitus and my eye cramps got worse, etc. I eventually had to reduce it back down to 20,000 iu, and I have been on about that dose ever since, as doses in between did not work out either.

My second check-up was with a new neurologist, a much quicker and better doctor, in my opinion. My very first MRI read, "Cannot exclude the possibility of progressive demyelinating illness", where as the second MRI, done about eleven months after the first MRI, and six months after I increased the vitamin D to an average of 20,000iu a day, said, «Cannot exclude demyelinating illness» So from the period before I started supplementing with 20,000 iu to 6 months after, it went from; «Suspicion of progressive demyelinating illness», to «Suspicion of demyelinating illness»

the word «progressive» was removed! There was no illness progression in eleven months, even on the lower dose of 20,000 iu a day! I also had severe fatigue, which is much better now. At the worst I would have energy for more than 2-3 hours a day and I would quickly be drained from just having simple conversations. My eyes would be small and very light sensitive. I still battle Endometriosis, which has been shown to not return after removing it with surgery (Laparoscopy) when continuing with supplementation of high doses of vitamin D3. Usually 2 out of 3 women who have this surgery will get Endometriosis back. When treated with high doses of Vitamin D3, there is a high rate of staying in remission.

Another great discovery I made last summer, after exploring the Coimbra Protocol, was to take a food gene test. It is called Nutrigenomics. It is a gene test that reveals what foods to eat for your specific genes, and it is absolutely genius to say the least, as now I am not easily sold on fad diets anymore, because I know what foods my body will tolerate. Another great revelation from the gene test was that one of my vitamin D3 receptors were defected. It is thought to be that forty percent

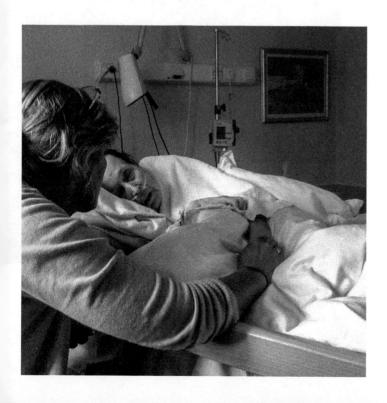

My mum paralyzed from her mouth and down lying in bed for 6 years

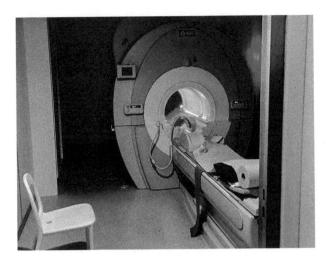

Having to lay in the MRI machine was a lesson in overcoming anxiety for me.

from that, I can only imagine that there is a very high number here in Norway too, or even higher percentage considering we are missing the sun for eight months of every year. And when it comes out there is no guarantee that it will be helping us produce any vitamin D3 at all. The gene test also indicates that a large number of people might not necessarily have autoimmune diseases, but defective vitamin D receptors. Which again can lead to autoimmune problems if not being supplemented with sufficient vitamin D3.

of the U.S. population has vitamin D3 deficiency. So if forty percent of the about 300 million people from one country suffers

This book is part of my health journey where my mission is to share the findings that have benefited me so they can benefit others who suffer with auto immune diseases and similar health issues.

My mum's funeral in 2013

About Vitamin D3, Coimbra & more

What is the Dr Coimbra High Dose Vitamin D3 Protocol?

Dr. Cicero Galli Coimbra is a neurologist and a professor practicing in São Paulo, Brazil. He has developed the Coimbra Protocol (CP) for suppression of auto immune diseases with high doses of vitamin D3. Dr. Coimbra has been able to successfully suppress disease activity in about 95% of auto immune cases with individually tailored doses of vitamin D3 plus other supplements such as magnesium and riboflavin (vitamin B2).

What types of Auto Immune Diseases have been treated with this Protocol?

Multiple Sclerosis (all types of MS), Arthritis Rheumatoid, Lupus, Lyme, Alopecia, Bronchitis, Depression, Atopic Depression, Crohn's Disease, Ulcerative Colitis, Hashimotos, Fibromyalgia, Hypertension, Infertility, Psoriasis, Ménière Syndromes, Ankylosing Spondylitis, Sjögrens Syndrome, Vitiligo, Endometriosis and many others.

What is Multiple Sclerosis (MS)?

Since the majority of people with MS are treated on the Coimbra Protocol, we will use the WebMD's definition of MS here; «MS happens when your immune system attacks a fatty material called myelin, which wraps around your nerve fibers to protect them. Without this outer shell, your nerves become damaged. Scar tissue may form».
The damage means your brain cannot send

«I think it's quite remarkable that Dr. Coimbra has so many patients that he has treated and that are responding really well to his protocol and therapy. This is a good starting point to think about starting clinical research studies that look into high-dose vitamin D3 for potentially helping patients with autoimmune diseases like multiple sclerosis.»

Dr. Michael Holick
A leading vitamin D researcher in the world, 2013

«When there is a deficiency of vitamin D3, the person can't regulate, which means stimulate or reduce, the activity of thousands of biological functions inside the cells of the immune system. The deficiency of this one substance amounts to a disaster for the immune system!»

Dr. Cicero Coimbra, Neurologist, PhD.

signals through your body correctly. Your nerves also do not work as they should to help you move and feel. As a result, you may have symptoms like:

- Trouble walking
- Feeling tired
- Muscle weakness or spasms
- Blurred or double vision
- Numbness and tingling
- Sexual problems
- Poor bladder or bowel control
- Pain
- Depression
- Problems focusing or remembering

Who SHOULD consider going on the protocol and WHO SHOULD NOT consider going on the protocol?

If you have an auto immune disease, you can consider starting with the CP. If you DO NOT have an autoimmune disease, then you can take up to 10 000 iu of vitamin D3 according to Dr Coimbra which he calls a paltry dose.

Does the protocol involve any specific diet?

You have to eat calcium restricted. That means that all dairy, calcium fortified or enriched products, most nuts and seeds must be avoided. There is calcium in many foods but the mentioned foods are the most important to avoid . It can be stressful to research all of this, that is why I wrote this book because there are people coming into the Vitamin D Lifestyle group on Facebook daily and are clueless of what to eat when starting out on the CP.

To learn more about the Coimbra Protocol you can sign up to this free email course online:

VitaminDLifestyle.com/CPstart

Coimbra Protocol FAQ

1. Is the Coimbra Protocol a diet?

No, the Dr. Coimbra Vitamin D3 Protocol is not a diet and is not focused on loosing weight. Although what you eat and especially what you cannot eat is an important part of the Coimbra Protocol. Weight-loss can however occur as a positive side effect.

2. Who is Dr. Coimbra and what does he do?

Dr. Cicero Galli Coimbra is a doctor from São Paulo, Brazil who has developed the Coimbra Protocol for the suppression of auto immune diseases. He has spend the last 20 years treating patients, using Vitamin D3, developing the Coimbra Protocol and training other doctors and nutritionists free of charge.

3. Will the Coimbra Protocol heal me from MS?

The Coimbra Vitamin D3 Protocol is a treatment for auto immune diseases not just MS. Although MS might not be completely reversed when already progressed far, the Coimbra Protocol has documented effect stopping the progress and reversing early stages of MS. Other auto immune diseases that are connected to lack of Vitamin D3 and that can be helped via the Coimbra Protocol are Arthritis Rheumatoid, Hashimotos, Lupus, Lyme, Alopecia, Bronchitis, Charcot-Marie-Tooth, Depression, Atopic Depression, Crohn's Disease, Endometriosis, Fibromyalgia, Hypertension, Infertility, Psoriasis, Ménière Syndromes, ADEM Syndromes, Sjögren, Vitiligo, Endometriosis and many others.

4. Is the Coimbra Protocol just about taking Vitamin D3?

A key part of the Dr. Coimbra Vitamin D3 Protocol is indeed Vitamin D3. As with any disease the exact treatment and dose thereof has to be considered individually for each patient. Under supervision of Protocol Doctors patients will try different high doses of Vitamin D3 over longer periods of time while abstaining from calcium rich food such as dairy, nuts and seeds.

5. How much Vitamin D3 can I take safely?

If you have an auto immune disease, you can consider going on the protocol. If you DO NOT have an autoimmune disease, then you can take up to 10 000 iu of Vitamin D3 per day according to Dr Coimbra which he calls a paltry dose. If you are on the protocol your Protocol Doctor will through tests determine how much Vitamin D3 you can take safely. This will change over time.

6. What kind of doses of Vitamin D3 are considered dangerously high?

This is very individual and very dependent on how much Calcium is in a patient's body.

Without supervision of a Protocol Doctor do not take more than 10 000 iu per day. While under strict supervision of calcium levels tested both in blood and urine patients of Dr Coimbra have taken much higher doses to great beneficial effect.

7. Is the Vitamin D3 or the calcium the problem?

There are many rumors saying that high doses of Vitamin D3 is dangerous. The true story is that it depends on the calcium levels of the patients. So the problem is high calcium and not high vitamin D3. Therefor Coimbra Protocol patients must strictly limit their intake of calcium and abstain from foods like milk, yogurt, cheese and nuts and dairy.

8. How do I check for high calcium levels?

Checks have to be done regularly every

couple of months. Checks involve 24h urine testing by a specialist laboratory. Your Protocol Specialist will help you with more information.

9. Can I do all of this alone or do I need a doctor?

You can not be on the Protocol without a Protocol Doctor / Protocol Specialist making sure you are safe and providing regular testing. Your general practitioners has most likely never heard anything about high doses of Vitamin D3 and therefor cannot help you. Several times each year Dr. Coimbra has trainings in Brazil to teach other doctors how the Protocol works (usually free of charge!)

10. What if my normal doctor does not want to help me?

Your normal doctor has most likely never heard anything about high doses of Vitamin D3 and can't help you. Most patients are either visiting Dr Coimbra in Brazil from time to time or are patients of one of the increasing number of Protocol Doctors worldwide. Many Protocol Doctors offer to treat patients via phone / online video conversations and provide information to patients and their local labs / doctors to facilitate regular testing.

11. Does the Coimbra Protocol treat fatigue?

Fatigue is one of the most common symptoms to leave within 6 weeks to 2 months of the Coimbra Protocol.

To learn more about the Coimbra Vitamin D3 Protocol sign up to the "15 day Coimbra Protocol Introduction Course on Email" at

VitaminDLifestyle.com/CPstart

Food Restrictions List

The most important foods related to controlling calcium in the diet

Allowed	
Bread	Fish
Butter, Mayonnaise	Eggs
Pasta (unless it includes cheese / cream or cream sauces)	Bananas
Rice	Teas, Coffee
Potatoes, Sweet potato, Cassava	Natural juices, Processed juices (unless they include soy)
Vegetables and raw leafy vegetables	Oat, oatmeal
Beans, Lentils, Peas, Chickpeas, Legumes (unless they include nuts / calcium)	Albumin
Cereals (unless they include nuts)	Gelatin, Jelly
Corn	Marshmallows
Mushrooms	Cakes, Cookies, Biscuits (unless they include filling / topping with milk or cream)
Fruits	

Moderate Consumption	Forbidden
Cheese bread (twice a week)	Milk, Condensed milk
Coconut water (1 glass a week)	Milk cream, Whipped cream
Coconut milk (200 ml per week)	Sour cream
Nuts, Walnuts, Almonds, Hazelnuts, Sunflower seeds (Total 1 tbsp per week)	Cheeses in general
Dark chocolate, 75% Cacao chocolate, Bittersweet chocolate,	White cheese, Sliced cheese, Cream cheese, Processed cheese, Goat cheese, Cottage cheese, Curd
Beer	Milkbased or cheesebased meals, Pizzas, Pies and Pastries
Wine	Yogurt
Distilled beverages	Soy, Soy milk, Soy cream, Soy juice
Açaí berries	Ricotta, Ricotta cream
Chicken meat *	Pudding, Rice pudding
Red meat *	Tofu, Tofu cream
Sausages **	Ice cream
	Cheese fondue
	Chocolate fondue
	Cheese pizzas in general
	Annona, Custard apple family
	Shanklish (milk cheese in Levantine cuisine)
	Sardine
	Rice milk (unless it is calcium free)
	Oat milk (unless it is calcium free)
	Corn milk (unless it is calcium free)

* Meat consumption has been discouraged due to a high level of heterocyclic amines produced during cooking. Heterocyclic amines are highly carcinogenic, so we suggest a moderate consumption of meat, especially chicken meat.

** All deli meats (salami, ham, sausage, frankfurter, turkey, mortadella,…) are rich in nitrosamines, which have a carcinogenic potential.

A HEALTHY OUTSIDE STARTS WITH A HEALTHY INSIDE.

Understanding Vitamin D3

Written by **Michael Cawley**
Coimbra Protocol Specialist

Vitamin D3 manufactured from sunlight and ingested in supplements is inactive until it is converted in the kidneys, bones, intestines and brain to 'activated' vitamin D3. Only activated Vitamin D3 reverses damage to myelin and suppresses auto immune activity. Inactive Vitamin D3 is of no medical value. Every person has a different level of vitamin D3 that their body is capable of converting.

When the body is given more Vitamin D3 than it can convert, the excess unconverted Vitamin D3 can sometimes be treated as an allergic compound and the body will manifest new symptoms of disease progression. These symptoms can include nausea, fatigue, light headedness, extreme weakness or even severe neurological problems. These symptoms disappear when the dose is lowered.

90% of auto immune patients have very high levels of vitamin D3 conversion but 10% do not. Generally high doses of vitamin D3 make auto immune patients feel great but for a small group of patients this is not the case.

Another tiny subset of patients cannot convert more than 10,000 iu of normal vitamin D3 either from sunshine or supplements. These patients usually thrive on micellized vitamin D3. Micellized vitamin D3 is converted in the lymph system instead of the usual conversion sites. The maximum amount of Vitamin D3 a person can naturally produce from a day's sun exposure is 20,000 iu. This dose, does not require blood tests or medical supervision in 99% of adults (once a calcium restricted diet is followed).

However a tiny number may not be aware that they have a problem with a serum calcium level that is always at a high normal. So for this reason I recommend that all people who choose to take 20,000iu daily, get a serum calcium and albumin test 4 weeks after starting 20,000 iu, just to

be certain you are safe from accidental calcium poisoning due to pre-existing kidney trouble. Otherwise don't take any risks and stay on 10,000 iu per day.

The reason Albumin needs to be checked is as follows,

Albumin is a protein commonly measured in blood. When it is high or low it can distort the serum calcium measurement making it appear either or lower than, it really is. When labs see albumin and serum calcium measured simultaneously they always give a 'corrected' or 'adjusted' calcium result which is always the more reliable result. Staying hydrated and avoiding milk, cheese, yogurt and nuts is mandatory to greatly reduce the risk of calcium toxicity. Even 20,000 iu (500mcg) of vitamin D3 with an adequate supply of magnesium can have life changing benefits for many auto immune patients in terms of slowing disease progression and improving quality of life.

Many newly diagnosed MS patients have experienced spectacular improvements on just 20,000 iu when it is combined with the right magnesiums, to read more about magnesium,the protocol and recommended products, go to www.Vitamindlifestyle.com

People without auto immune problems gain significant health protection when supplementing with 10,000 iu (250mcg) per day.
For normal healthy people Dr Coimbra recommends 10 000 iu a day.

DISCLAIMER:

The Miracle and Importance of Magnesium

Written by **Michael Cawley**,
Coimbra Protocol Specialist.

Magnesium is an essential mineral found in green vegetables, nuts, beans and seafood. Magnesium transports Vitamin D3 around the body and helps to convert vitamin D3 from inactive to active. For this reason, it is a critical partner of Vitamin D3 in helping prevent and control auto immune illness. The daily consumption of doses of Vitamin D3 above 20,000 iu (500mcg) per day will increase the bodies magnesium requirements.

If high doses of vitamin D3 are taken for extended periods of time without adequate magnesium in diet and supplements then the following symptoms can emerge, bone pain, weakness, insomnia, palpitations and anxiety. In the world of magnesium it's all about purity and bioavailability.

The higher the quality of magnesium you use the less vitamin D3 will be needed to manage your disease and the more likely you are to notice significant benefits from Vitamin D3 supplementation.

You can read about pure magnesiums on the website Vitamindlifestyle.com at this direct link: https://vitamindlifestyle. com/the-miracle-and-importance-with-magnesium-on-the-coimbra-protocol/

DISCLAIMER:

This article is not intended to provide diagnosis, treatment or medical advice. Content provided on this post is for informational purposes only. Please consult with a trained Protocol Coimbra Specialist regarding any diagnosis or treatment options.

Vitamin D3 for kids

"The dose of 10,000 IU per day is considered by all researchers, by all international vitamin D3 experts, NOAEL (No Adverse Effect Level). It means there is no negative side effect with this dose of vitamin D3 in an adult person.

When we talk about children (not on the Protocol, but normal healthy kids), we have to make a correction through weight: a child at birth, independently of the weight, can receive 1,000 IU per day. When he/she reaches 10 kg of weight, the dose increases to 2,000 IU. With 15 kg, 3,000 IU, that is to say, every 5 kg of weight the dose increases by 1,000 IU, until the child reaches 50 kg and starts to take 10,000 IU, which he/she can take indefinitely.

People living in an urban environment are not exposed to the sun, they are not able to expose a body area large enough to produce the required amount of vitamin D3. This is very serious, for all of our cells, without exception, need vitamin D3 to stay healthy."

Cícero Galli Coimbra, Neurologist, Ph.D.

REJOICING IS AN ACT OF THE WILL AND NOT AN ACT OF YOUR FEELINGS.

Graham Cooke

Food Planning

Food planning can be a headache for most of us - especially when we have never done it or don't know how to do it or as in many cases for people with disabilities and the elderly, that they will need to have someone to help them.

Well first of all I am the first to admit that I am currently no expert in this area but I am working in it. When eating low calcium foods you will need to plan to a certain degree to make this work. So I will share with you some strategies that can be helpful for you.

1. Plan ahead.

Take some of the food planning friendly dinners and other meals in this book and find out which ones you want to eat. Make batches of our each meal. For example if you want to make some of the soups to freeze down calculate how many dinners you will have to make and how much you will have to buy. Find out if you want to make it first and then freeze it down or if you just want to chop it up and make it out of zip lock bags from the freezer.

2. Ask for help

If you are sick, disabled or just have little energy (or just in general), buying, cutting those vegetables and fruits can be a big job, and it is of course best if you can buy already organic chopped fruits and vegetables from the store. Still you need help to put it into different zip lock bags etc. Asking help from a nearby church, organization or school could be an option. Maybe you can pay some young adults that will come and help you food plan up every 14 days. I am just throwing out some ideas you can run with.

3. Have a combination of foods available

It is good to have a combination of foods ready to defrost from the freezer, pre made fresh food that can last up to days in the fridge and foods you can take out and make immediately plus left overs.

4. Buy good tools

Have good tools you can work with that

takes the hard work out of your food planning. Get good quality chopping knives, good machines such as blender and food processor. Have zip lock bags and ice cube silicone forms available.

5. Set aside time

When you start this thing set aside enough time and do not stress. It might take all of your day, or at least most of the energy you had that day. Still, you will be on your way to success in your food planning eating regime. No one will master your fort like you do!

6. Let the journey transform you!

That sounded really weird, right? Haha you will see what happens when you start. You will think about foods like never before and why you eat them, the combination of the tastes and the nutrition and why you haven't done this before. Let the journey transform you into a master over your life. Take back control and enjoy it!

If you want to learn more and get support, join us on the free clean eating challenge, sign up to this link here: outstandinghealth.com

Grocery Shopping Guide

Produce

Sweet Potatoes

Avocado

Cauliflower

Zucchini

Kale

Eggs

Vegetables (for roasting/cooking)

Carrots

Celery

Onions/ Scallions

Bell Peppers

Tomatoes

Cherry Tomatoes

Garlic

Apples

Bananas

Berries

Grapes

Meat

Chicken Breasts

Cow/Turkey/Chicken minced

Nitrate Free/ Uncured/ Unprocessed Bacon

Fish- Salmon

Lamb

Dairy Replacement

Unsweetened, oat milk that is not calcium fortified

Unsweetened, coconut milk that is not calcium fortified

Unsweetened, rice milk that is not calcium fortified

Tip: So think in many places to use coconut oil instead of butter and coconut milk instead of cream.

Also look for a non calcium fortified oat cream replacement for cream if they have in your country.

Gelatin Powders

Great Lakes Gelatin Co., Collagen Hydrolysate, Collagen Joint Care, Beef, 16 oz (454 g) (for smoothies etc)

Now Foods, Real Food, Beef Gelatin Powder, 1 lb (454 g) (for making gelatin figures etc)

Great Lakes Gelatin Co., Beef Hide Gelatin, Collagen Joint Care, Unflavored, 16 oz (454 g) ((for making gelatin figures etc)

Tip: I buy these from iherb.com

Protein Powders

MRM, Veggie Elite, Performance Protein, Vanilla Bean, 2.2 lbs (1,020 g) (this brand has more low calcium options and clean tastes etc)
Only 3 % calcium per serving

MRM, Veggie Elite, Performance Protein, Cinnamon Bun, 36 oz (1,020 g) only 3 % calcium per serving

MRM, Natural Egg White Protein, Vanilla, 24 oz (680 g) only 3 % calcium per serving

Tip: I buy these from iherb.com type the name in and you should find them. Also check if Amazon has them

Continues on next page.

Baking/Staples/Spices

Maple Syrup

Agave Syrup

Honey

Chocolate Chips

Unsweetened Raw Cocoa Powder (insert link)

Whole Grain Flour

Unsweetened Coconut Flakes

Vanilla Extract

Himalayan salt

Garlic Powder

Onion Powder

Chili Powder

Cumin

Cayenne

Ginger, ground

Turmeric, ground

Chili flakes

Cinnamon, ground

Cardamom, ground

Clove, ground

Nutmeg, ground

Allspice, ground

Baking Powder

Baking Soda

Minced Garlic

Olive Oil

Coconut Oil

Shredded, Unsweetened Coconut

Frozen

Frozen Broccoli

Frozen Chopped Bananas

Frozen Strawberries/Raspberries

Frozen Mango

Frozen Blueberries

Frozen Ice cubes

Frozen Ice cubes made from coffee

Canned

Tomatoes, peeled with garlic and basil

Chili

Tomato Paste

Canned Corn

Canned Beans

Pineapple in chunks

Pantry/Other

Popcorn Kernels

Crisp Bread

Rye Bread (Pumper nickel bread)

Asian Fish Sauce

Vegetable stock

Lemon grass (in a glass)

Whole-Grain Tortillas

Curry paste

Oatmeal

Pine nuts

Pumpkin Seeds

Milk Allergy and Lactose Intolerance

Even though there are some foods like cakes, cookies, biscuits and bread that are on the allowed list on the Food Restriction List (see page ?) there are people who have milk allergy and lactose intolerance and would need to avoid these foods.

Cow milk allergy is the most common food allergy in children, according to FARE (Food Allergy Research & Education), with symptoms ranging from hives, vomiting, diarrhea, wheezing, runny nose, to the most severe, anaphylaxis.

Having an intolerance to lactose (the sugar in milk) indicates the absence of the enzyme lactase, which is needed to digest lactose. This is different from a milk allergy because the immune system is not activated.

Common symptoms of lactose intolerance include:

- Painful Gas
- Stomach pain and discomfort
- Bloating
- Nausea
- Diarrhea

Hidden Sources of Dairy

For People with Milk Allergy and Lactose Intolerance

Sources of Dairy

Milk (all forms: condensed, cow, derivative, dry, evaporated, goat, low fat, malted, nonfat, powder, protein, sheep, skim, solids, whole)

Butter (acid, ester, fat, flavor, oil)

Buttermilk

Casein

Caseinates (all forms)

Cheese (cow, goat, sheep)

Cottage Cheese

Cream (including whipped)

Curds

Custard

Dairy Milk Solids

Diacetyl

Galactose

Ghee

Half and Half

Hydrolysates

Lactalbumin

Lactate Solids

Lactoferrin

Lactogluobulin

Lactose

Lactulose

Lactyc Yeast

Magnesium Caseinate

Nougat

Potassium Caseinate

Pudding

Quark

Recaldent

Rennet Casein

Simplesse (fat replacer)

Sour Cream (solids & imitation)

Sour Milk Solids

Tagatose

Whey (all forms)

Whipped Topping

Yogurt (regular & frozen)

Yogurt Powder

Zinc Caseinate

Foods and Ingredients that MAY contain Dairy

Artificial butter Flavour

Artificial Flavouring

Artificial Sweeteners

Baby Formulas

Baked Goods

Baking Mixes

Batter Fried foods

Bread

Breath Mints

Candy

Caramel Candies

Caramel Flavouring

Cereal

Chewing Gum

Chicken Broth

Chocolate

Coffee Creamer

Cream Liqueurs

Cream Sauces

Cream Based Soups

Eggnog

Fat Replacers

Fondue

Gravy/Gravy Mixes

Lactic Acid Starter Culture

High Protein Flour

Hot Dogs

Hydrolyzed Vegetable Protein

Imitation Sour Cream

Imitation Maple & Other Syrups

Instant Mashed Potatoes

Kosher Parve Desserts

Margarine

Natural Flavouring

Nisin

Nondairy Products/Milk Substitutes

Be also aware that lactose is used as the base for more than 20% of prescription drugs and about 6% of over the counter

Eating Suggestions For Weight Control

This diet plan focuses on healthy and predominantly clean eating without subscribing to any specific diet, but will comply with the Coimbra Protocol restrictions.

Have 3 regular meals and add a mini meal or a snack between lunch and dinner and before bedtime (preferably the last meal no later than 2-3 hours before bedtime). If you eat breakfast more than 5 hours before your lunch, eat an apple or fruit etc in between to keep your blood sugars stable.

Preferably should every meal and mini- meal contain healthy organic free range protein, healthy non- processed fats and healthy non processed carbs.

If you want to focus on weight control you will have to watch your portions. A rule of thumb to follow to maintain this is that your protein and carb servings should never be larger than your fist and fat should be about the size of your thumb. However, I do eat avocado and salmon larger than my thumb, hehe.

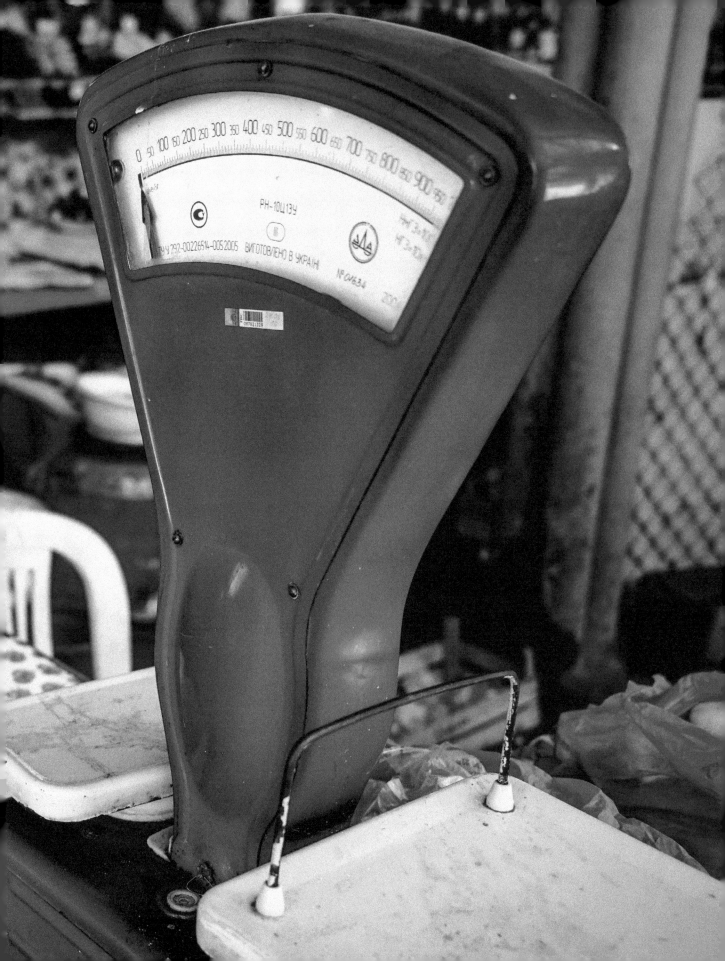

Units of Measurement: Common Abbreviations

C, c
= cup

g
= gram

kg
= kilogram

L, l
= liter

lb
= pound

mL, ml
= milliliter

oz
= ounce

pt
= pint

t, tsp
= teaspoon

T, TB, Tbl, Tbsp
= tablespoon

WHEN I LOST ALL MY
EXCUSES, I FOUND ALL MY
RESULTS.

Staple Foods & Stuff

Crisp bread

Crisp bread (or "knekkebrød" in Norwegian) is a traditional Scandinavian bread type that is over 1500 years old. This special thin and dry like a cracker kind of bread was invented to last through the long Scandinavian winters as it says eatable for month and thus baked just twice a year.

Traditionally made of wholegrain rye flour, salt and water only, many kinds of crisp bread can be found today containing spices like dill, grains and seeds like sesame, yeast and sourdough.

Crisp bread baked with wholegrain flour is a healthy and natural foundation for all kind of spreads with health benefits over wheat bread / white bread.

Health benefits of crisp bread:

(Strongest in wholegrain crisp bread)

*   Very high in fiber thus promotes regular bowel movements and helps prevent constipation
*   Variety of whole grains are an important source of antioxidants, vitamins, phytoestrogens and minerals
*   Low in fat and saturated fat
*   High in protein

If crisp bread seems hard to find in your area buy from ikea.com (under Products -> Food -> Bread & Dairy).

Crisp bread made from white / refined wheat flour is not recommended for clean eating.

THE ORIGINAL

OAT-LY!

ØKOLOGISK HAVRE DRIKK

No milk.
No soy.
No ...eh...
whatever.

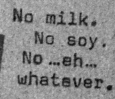
it's Swe-dish!

1 L   0,5% fett

Dairy Replacement Milks

Drinking calcium restricted milks means 100% dairy free but there is also calcium in other healthy drinks such as almond milk.

Milks such as oat milk, rice milk and coconut milk are allowed on the protocol. Oat milk is one of my favorite that I use on a daily basis.

A good rule of thumb is, always look for and avoid «calcium fortified». Products that are organic are not supposed to be fortified with anything, that is the whole point of being organic.

Himalayan Salt

As a natural source of sodium, Himalayan salt provides an essential mineral for healthy bodily functions. Sodium helps to regulate blood volume and thus blood pressure, as well as helping to control muscle contractions, nerve transmissions and heart functions. Sodium can be found naturally in a number of foods, but it can also be consumed as added salt, as in the case of Himalayan salt. The daily recommended amount of sodium to be consumed daily is between 1500 mg and 2300 mg, for men and women between the ages of 9 and 50.

Himalayan salt is widely touted for its mineral content, containing 84 minerals in total. In addition to sodium, Himalayan salt is relatively high in iron, magnesium, phosphorus, calcium, potassium and chloride. It also contains traces of boron, fluoride, iodine, zinc, selenium and copper, all of which are necessary for bodily health. As a naturally occurring salt, Himalayan salt contains all these minerals without chemical processing or refinement. Because it is harvested naturally, Himalayan salt's mineral benefits are available regardless of what form the salt is consumed as. Himalayan salt is most commonly found as coarse grains, fine grains, or large blocks which can be used as serving platters that delicately "season" the food they serve.

Despite its high mineral content, Himalayan salt is primarily a source of sodium, and excess sodium consumption can lead to a host of health problems. The most well known of these complications is hypertension, or high blood pressure. When sodium levels rise, your body retains water in an attempt to dilute the blood, increasing blood volume and pressure. As sodium naturally occurs in a wide range of foods, eating too much added sodium, even in the form of Himalayan salt, can be more detrimental than beneficial to your overall health. Limit your sodium consumption to no more than 2300 mg per day, or 1500 mg per day, if you suffer from high blood pressure.

Pumpernickel Rye Bread

Pumpernickel or "Schwarzbrot" ("Black bread" in German) is traditionally made with sourdough and coarsely ground rye. Wholegrain rye contains higher concentrations of dietary fiber and other nutrients and has health benefits usually not associated with refined wheat flour or any other kind of bread.

Traditionally rye bread is baked at low temperatures for long periods of time giving the bread it's typical dark color and a unique, heavy, sourdough yet slightly sweet taste.

There are different types of rye bread, some of which drop the sourdough and include additional malt or even coffee to make the bread darker and create variations in taste. You can try them and find your favorite.

Health benefits of rye bread:

(Strongest in wholegrain rye bread)

- Promotes regular bowel movements and helps prevent constipation
- Contains soluble fiber which binds cholesterol and reduces risk of heart disease
- Reduces risk of type 2 diabetes
- Low to medium glycemic index (depending on ingredients) thus less likely to increase blood sugar level compared to white bread
- Contains B-complex vitamins like thiamine and niacin
- Contains even less calcium than wheat bread.

Stevia - a sugar substitute

I use some stevia drops in my coffee, and the «Nice Creams» amongst others.

The good thing about Stevia is that it doesn't add calories and unlike other sugar substitutes, Stevia is derived from a plant called Stevia rebaudiana
It is about 150 times sweeter than sugar in the same concentration.

Source: Wikipedia

Other Sweeteners

Other sources for sweeteners are **honey** and **maple syrup**.

Terrific Taco Seasoning

Now you can make your own great and affordable taco seasoning without sugar, flavor enhancers and other additives! In the recipe book you will find it added in the meat with a healthier alternative as in the Stuffed Bell Pepper Recipe.

Ingredients

3 Tablespoons of chili powder
2 1/2 teaspoons of chili pepper flakes, crushed
2 teaspoons Cayenne pepper
2 Tablespoons paprika powder
2 1/2 teaspoons dried oregano
2 Tablespoons cumin, ground
2 teaspoons garlic powder
2 Tablespoons Himalayan salt
0,5 teaspoon of ginger, ground

This is how we use the Taco Seasoning in the meat:

Cook the meat in butter/oil and sprinkle 2 Tablespoons of Taco seasoning over. Mix well. After a few minutes, add the finely chopped onions and garlic and leave to simmer until the meat is thoroughly cooked. Add in the water and allow to simmer for a few minutes more. If you want it stronger, taste to with more of the Terrific Taco Seasoning.

Vanessa's Spice Mix

For my spice mix, the formula is not that super secret. I take about equal parts of my favorite spices except from chili flakes and cayenne which I take about half.

I use spices in glass jars or bags bought from the local shop.

Ingredients

Cayenne pepper
Paprika (bell pepper)
Ginger
Garlic Salt Powder
Pepper (ground)
And I at times add curry and cumin

Play around with it and make your own spice mix.
Perhaps you don't like it hot at all, I sure do!

Beef Gelatin Powder

Natural Thickening Agent
Good Source of Protein

NET WT. 1 LB. (454 g)

your recipe's secret ingredient

Beef Gelatin Pow

Nutrition Facts

Serving Size about 1 Tbsp (10 g)
Servings Per Container about 45

Amount Per Serving	
Calories 35	Calories from Fat 0

	%Daily Value*
Total Fat 0g	0%
Saturated Fat 0g	0%
Trans Fat 0g	
Cholesterol 0mg	0%
Sodium 20mg	<1%
Total Carbohydrate 0g	0%
Dietary Fiber 0g	0%
Sugars 0g	
Protein 9g	18%

Vitamin A	0%	Vitamin C	0%
Calcium	0%	Iron	0%

* Percent Daily Values are based on a 2,000 calorie diet.

Ingredients: Pure Beef Gelatin.

Distributed by NOW FOODS
Bloomingdale, IL 60108, USA
www.nowrealfood.com

NOW Real Food™ 1
Gelatin is a natura
and texturizer that
soaking necessary
used in jams, jellie
marshmallows, an
It's often used to c
adding a lot of calc

Mix 1 tablespoon i
juice and consume
also be used to ma
desserts by adding
and then adding sw
ice per cookbook d

Because you are what
Food™ has been comm
delicious, healthy, natur
foods since 1968. We'r
family owned, and prou
natural. Keep it real.

MOISTURE RAISED

Pure Unflavored Protein
Kosher Beef

NEW LOOK!

GREAT LAKES GELATIN

Collagen Hydrolysate

COLLAGEN DIETARY SUPPLEMENT

Collagen Joint Care

Net weight 16 oz (1 LB) 454 grams

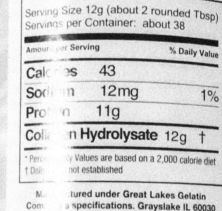

Supplement Facts

Serving Size 12g (about 2 rounded Tbsp)
Servings per Container: about 38

Amount per Serving		% Daily Value
Calories	43	
Sodium	12mg	1%
Protein	11g	
Collagen Hydrolysate	12g	†

* Percent Daily Values are based on a 2,000 calorie diet.
† Daily not established

Manufactured under Great Lakes Gelatin
Company's specifications. Grayslake IL 60030

Ingredients: **Hydrolyzed Collagen**

Recommended Dosage: Take two rounded
tablespoons (12g) twice a day.

Recommended Uses: This product has a low
molecular weight so it will dissolve in cold,
warm or hot liquids. Collagen Hydrolysate as a
pure protein taken before meals may help curb
appetite. Enjoy when added to your favorite
drink such as coffee, smoothies, non-carbonated
beverages or juice.

HOT OR

COLLAGE

Hydrolyzed
body's metab
molecular
digestive tract

The rapid ab
groups in this
number of ma

The body's na
connective tissue
cartilage, skin, h
one's mid-twen
acids such as gly
are important am
the body to buil
support the h

Hydrolyzed coll
naturally in the
bioactive prote
easily assimila

Hydrolyzed coll
of amino acids
molecular

What is Gelatin?

Gelatin is a mixture of peptides and proteins produced by partial hydrolysis of collagen extracted from the skin, bones, and connective tissues of animals such as domesticated cattle, chicken, pigs, and fish. The reason it's used in food preparation and as the basis of many jellies, desserts and candies is because it acts like a sticky adhesive, similar to a natural glue. The gelatinous quality of gelatin is actually one of the things that makes it beneficial when we consume it, because this is what allows gelatin to help form strong cartilage or connective tissue that gives parts of our bodies elasticity.

In this book we have used Great Lakes Gelatin Co., Collagen Hydrolysate, Collagen Joint Care, Beef to add to smoothies etc.

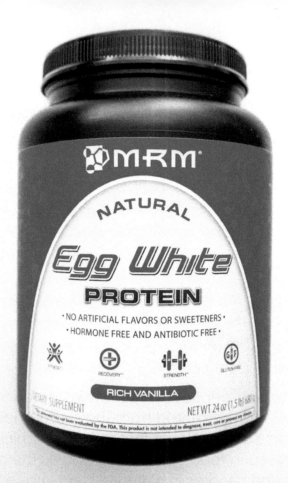

Directions: Add one slightly heaping scoop to 12oz of water or your favorite beverage and shake or blend for 30-60 seconds. Use one serving daily to add protein to your diet.

Supplement Facts

Serving Size 1 Scoop (approx. 33 grams)
Servings Per Container - 20

Amount Per Serving		% Daily Value*
Calories	100	
Calories from Fat	0	
Total Fat	0g	0%
Saturated Fat	0g	0%
Trans Fat	0g	†
Cholesterol	0mg	0%
Sodium	370mg	15%
Potassium	330mg	9%
Total Carbohydrates	2g	1%
Dietary Fiber	0g	0%
Sugars	0g	†
Protein	23g	46%
Vitamin A	0 IU	0%
Vitamin C	0mg	0%
Calcium	26mg	3%
Iron	72mcg	<1%
Riboflavin	680mcg	40%
Phosphorus	30mg	3%

*Percent Daily Values are based on a 2,000 calorie diet.
†Daily Value not established.

Typical Amino Acid Profile Per 33g Serving

Alanine	1410mg
Arginine	1340mg
Aspartic Acid	2330mg
Cysteine	630mg
Glutamic Acid	2970mg
Glycine	790mg
Histidine	530mg
Isoleucine	1220mg
Leucine	1940mg
Lysine	1450mg
Methionine	860mg
Phenylalanine	1340mg
Proline	880mg
Serine	1570mg
Threonine	1040mg
Tryptophan	370mg
Tyrosine	900mg
Valine	1570mg

- **No MSG**
- **No Aspartame or Acesulfame K**

Other Ingredients: Instantized Egg Albumen, Natural Vanilla Flavor, Sunflower Lecithin, Stevia Leaf Extract, Xanthan Gum, Monk Fruit Extract and Digest-ALL® AP (a vegan enzyme blend).

Contains NO added

Please

What Are Protein Powders?

Protein powders are what you add to liquid like oat milk etc to make a protein powder shake. These can be used to add extra protein to your diet. A lot of the foods we have accessible that do not need cooking are carbohydrates. These are good sources of protein in addition to lean protein like meat, fish and chicken etc

Protein powders come in various forms. The three common ones are whey, soy, and casein protein.
However, the before mentioned types of protein powders can cause allergic or undesired reactions, that is why I choose protein powders from egg white and hemp, - also because these are low in calcium.

Protein powders are also used for athletes to help them in a healing process, teenagers who are growing, people who are going vegan and when you are starting a workout program. It is also a good source of protein when you have to cut out dairy of your diet.

OTTO'S

CASSAVA FLOUR

GLUTEN-FREE
GRAIN-FREE
NUT-FREE

100% YUCA ROOT

32 oz (2 lb) 907g (.91Kg) ℮

GRAIN-FREE JUST GOT EASY!

GLUTEN-FREE, SINGLE-INGREDIENT WHOLE-FOOD PALEO FLOUR

Do you miss your grandma's apple pie or mom's homemade tortillas? What if we told you that you can re-create delicious, grain-free versions of all your favorite family recipes that actually taste like you remember them? Well, that's exactly what we're telling you. Our cassava flour can be used as a one-to-one substitute for wheat flour in many traditional recipes because of its mild flavor and light texture. How exciting is that?!

Cassava — pronounced [kuh-sah-vuh] and also known as Yuca — has been a staple food around the world for centuries. What sets us apart from tapioca is that we dry and grind this sustainable root vegetable using the whole root, not just the extracted starch. It's free of grains and gluten, nuts and soy. No additives, xanthan gum, or fillers either!

If that's not a baking revolution, we don't know what is.

We can't wait for you to try our flour. When you do, please share your creations with us on Instagram by tagging @Ottos_Cassava_Flour.

HAPPY BAKING!

Grain Free Tortillas

Recipe courtesy of:
Cara of ForkandBeans.com
Makes about 6 tortillas.

AIP/ PALEO/ VEGAN!

Ingredients
- ¾ c. (96g) Otto's Naturals Cassava flour
- ¼ tsp. sea salt
- 2 Tbsp. olive oil
- ½ c. (80g) warm water

Instructions:
1. Whisk together the flour and salt. Add the oil and warm...

3. Roll each dough ball between two pieces of parchment paper until thin. Or use a tortilla press.

4. Heat a dry skillet over medium high heat. Once properly heated, place tortilla on skillet. Wait for the air bubbles to form (approx. 1

Nutrition Facts

about 28 servings per container

Serving size	1/4 cup (32g)

Amount per serving

Calories	110

	% Daily Value*
Total Fat 0g	0%
Saturated Fat 0g	0%
Trans Fat 0g	
Cholesterol 0mg	0%
Sodium 0mg	0%
Total Carbohydrate 28g	10%
Dietary Fiber 3g	11%
Total Sugars 0g	
Includes 0g Added Sugars	0%
Protein 1g	
Vitamin D 0mcg	0%
Calcium 32mg	2%
Iron 0mg	0%
Potassium 83mg	2%

*The % Daily Value tells you how much a nutrient in a serving of food contributes to a daily diet. 2,000 calories a day is used for general nutrition advice.

Calories per gram:
Fat 9 • Carbohydrate 4 • Protein 4

Ingredients: 100% Cassava (yuca root)

No Refrigeration Necessary

**Product of Brazil
Packed in the USA for**

Otto's Naturals
1802 State Route 31 Ste 124
Clinton, NJ, 08809
Ph: 732.654.OTTO (6886)
ottosnaturals.com

Allergen Info:
Free of Dairy, Eggs, Gluten,
Peanuts, Soy and Tree Nuts.

Cassava Flour

Cassava flour is what I prefer to use as an alternative to wheat flour. It has a consistency and texture that is great for baking, closely resembling wheat flour. It is however completely gluten-free, grain-free and nut-free and great if you are looking for an alternative.

Cassava is widely used in South-America, parts of Asia and Africa for both breads, cakes and dishes. It is usable for vegan, vegetarian as well as paleo diets.

You are free to experiment with Cassava flour or any other low-calcium flour to find the consistency and taste you prefer.

Breakfast

Breakfast

Bread Spreads

Bacon & Egg Breakfast

Avo Tuna

Egg Cupcakes

Exotic Smoothie Bowl

Mango Strawberry Smoothie Bowl

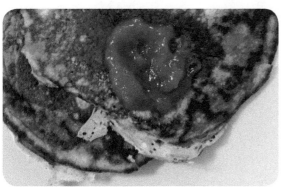

Protein Pancake

Oatmeal Bowl

 Vegan   Vegetarian   Gluten free

Bread Spreads

Rye bread and crisp bread with spreads of sliced strawberries, eggs, cucumber, tomatoes, kiwis, bananas, avocados, clementine boats, blueberries and pineapple rings.

 Vegetarian

Bacon & Egg Breakfast

Some people like to start their day with eating high fats to get their fat metabolism started. They eat breakfast like a king, lunch like a prince and dinner like a pauper. So the aim is to start with a heavier meal when your metabolism is on the highest like in the morning. Anyways, here is a break fast that is full in fats and I have eaten in certain periods of my life.

This is how we do it.

Ingredients

2-4 bacon strips, cooked
1-2 eggs, cooked
1/2 tin of sliced mushrooms, cooked
3-6 halved cherry tomatoes, cooked
1/2 avocado

When cooked, then ready to serve and eat immediately

 Gluten free

Avo Tuna

Ingredients

1 can of tuna in water, remove the water
1 big avocado
1 Tablespoon squeezed lemon
1 Tablespoon mayonnaise
Taste to with Himalayan salt and pepper
1 teaspoon garlic salt (optional)
Chili flakes (optional)

This is how you do it:

Sift the water out off the tuna. Part the avocado into two halves and remove the stone and peel. Add everything into the food processor and blend it all together (or use a fork to mash it). Taste to with spices and serve on rye bread or crisp bread.

Tip: It can last up to 5 days in the refrigerator so you might want to make a bigger portion when you are first at it.

Vegetarian   Gluten free

Egg Cupcakes

Ingredients

7 eggs
5-6 diced cherry tomatoes
3 mini paprikas (peppers) chopped
Some chives, chopped
About 2 big mushrooms chopped
1 cloves garlic add more if you like
12 cooked bacon strips (optional)
2 teaspoons (flat) of grounded cumin
Himalayan salt to taste
Peppers to taste
Olive oil (remember to oil properly the cupcake pan)

This is how we do it.

1. Preheat the oven to 350F / 180 C.
2. Grease a 12 count cupcake pan,
   or line them with parchment paper.
3. If you choose to add the optional bacon, then add a slice of
   bacon around the edge of each cupcake (so it will wrap around
   the egg mixture)
4. Whisk together egg, onion, spices and add the tomatoes, mushrooms, chives, peppers and pour into the cupcake form. You can
   also just whisk the eggs and the spices and add the veggies after
   by hand to the cupcake form instead.
5. Bake for 15-20 minutes.

 Gluten free

Exotic Smoothie Bowl

Ingredients

1 frozen banana
1/4 of frozen mango
1 dl/ 0.4 cups of blueberries
1 dl/ 0.4 cups of strawberries or raspberries
2 dl/ 0,8 cups of oat milk
1 Tablespoon Vanilla Protein powder of choice with low calcium
1 Tablespoon Great Lakes Gelatin Collagen Hydrolysate (optional)

Mango Strawberry Smoothie Bowl

Ingredients

1 frozen banana
1/4 of frozen mango
1 dl/ 0.8 cups of frozen strawberries
2 dl/ 0,8 cups of oat milk
1 Tablespoon MRM, Natural Egg White Protein with Vanilla flavor or any low calcium vanilla protein powder of choice
1 Tablespoon Great Lakes Gelatin Collagen Hydrolysate (optional)

 Vegan  Vegetarian  Gluten free

Protein Pancake

About 2-3 pancakes

Ingredients

6 egg whites
165 ml of coconut milk (a little can)
6 Tablespoons of rolled oats
3 teaspoons of vanilla protein powder of your choice low calcium
1 teaspoon baking powder
1 teaspoon vanilla extract/powder/essence
1/2 teaspoon cinnamon

This is how we do it:

Combine egg whites, protein powder and coconut milk in a blender. Blend until smooth and combined. Add remaining ingredients and blend again until it is creamy. Cook in a non-stick pan over medium heat for 2-3 mins per side until golden brown. Serve with for example fresh berries, coconut sugar, 2 teaspoons of coconut milk (which is not overly liquid).

Tip: For dessert you can add some chocolate sauce. Take 50 grams of 86% dark chocolate melt it, add some coconut oil and for example 5 drops of orange essential oil or a few drops of the stevia drops such as hazelnut, English toffee etc.

 Vegan  Vegetarian Gluten free

Oatmeal Bowl

Ingredients

70 grams of rolled oats
Water to boil
1 pinch cinnamon
1 pinch honey
1/2 avocado sliced (optional)
Grapes (optional)
Blueberries (optional)

This is how we do it

Boil the oat as instructed on the back of the package with water. Set aside and pour into a bowl. Add cinnamon, honey, avocado, grapes, blueberries or anything you want to add such as bananas etc and serve immediately.

 Vegan  Vegetarian Gluten free

Lunches &
Small Dinners

Lunches & Small Dinners

Mason Jar Salads

Pin Wheels

Lentil Patties

**Mango and
Sweet Potato Salad**

Cauliflower Rice Snack

**Immune Boosting
Soup**

Tomato Soup

Winter soup

Yummy Lentil Soup

 Vegan Vegetarian  Gluten free

Mason Jar Salads

Chicken and Bean Salad

Serves 3

400-600 grams of chicken breast,
sliced and cooked.
1 can of black beans
1 small can corn
1 can of pine apple in chunks
4 radishes sliced
3 chives chopped
1 bag of salad mix
8 halved cherry tomatoes
1/2 red onion, chopped
1 cucumber, chopped
1 big avocado, pitted, peeled and
sliced (optional)

This is how you do it:
Toss together the greens in a bowl.
Add the chicken on top.

Tuna and Bean Salad

Serves 3

2 cans of tuna (in water)
1 can of black beans
1/2 tin of pine apple in chunks
1 bag of salad mix
8 halved cherry tomatoes
1/2 red onion, chopped
1 cucumber, chopped
1 big avocado, pitted, peeled and
sliced
10-12 Calamatta olives, halved

This is how you do it:
Sift the water off the tuna. Toss together the rest of the chopped and
sliced in a bowl. Garnish with olives.

Mason Jar Salad

Serves 3

Iceberg salad, chopped
2-3 radishes, chopped
8 cherry tomatoes, halved
1/4 cauliflower, chopped into small
pretty bouquets :)
3-4 shredded carrots
Half a box of chopped pineapple
A bundle of chives, chopped into
small pieces
Dill or parsley (optional)

Dressing
1 Tablespoon mustard
1 Tablespoon honey
1 Tablespoon olive oil
1 Tablespoon water
2 Tablespoon light balsamic
Pepper and Himalayan salt

This is how we do it:
Add the salad in a big mason jar or
divide evenly in four bowls. Whisk
the dressing together and keep it in
a little container by itself and pour it
over the salad before eating.

Pin Wheels

Ingredients per wrap

2 big gluten free tortillas wraps or similar
100 grams of shaved chicken or turkey (for bread spread).
1 Teaspoon mustard
Lettuce

This is how we do it:

Put everything on the tortillas and roll them up together. Cut them into rolls. Use toothpick or similar to hold together.

Tip: Use lettuce as wrapping instead of tortilla wraps for a more healthy option. Add in the vegetables you want and find your own favorites.

 Gluten free

Lentil Patties

Ingredients

2 dl (0.85 cups) red lentils
2 eggs
1/2 chopped yellow onion
2 Tablespoons of any healthy gluten free flour that is low in calcium based
1/2 teaspoon Turmeric
1 Tablespoon Cumin
1 clove garlic, minced
A pinch Himalayan salt

This is how we do it:

Boil the lentils with double the water. When they are boiled through, sift out the surplus water. Let it chill down, and then add in the eggs, onions, garlic, turmeric, cumin and salt. Add some olive oil in heating pan, and form small patties with table spoons.

 Vegan Vegetarian Gluten free

Mango and
Sweet Potato Salad

Ingredients

1 large sweet potato
1 mango peeled and cut into dices
1 red bell pepper/capsicum, seeded and shopped
1 avocado, peeled, seeded and cut into dices

This is how you do it:

Preheat oven to 400F/200 C. Use the a fork to prick the potato all over. Place potato on a small baking sheet to catch any drips. Place in oven and roast until a knife can easily pierce through the middle of the potato, about 45 minutes. Let potato cool to room temperature (you don't have to, I just put them in the salad warm). Peel the sweet potato, cut into dices and place in a medium bowl. Add the mango, avocado, bell pepper and chicken if you choose to add it. Voila, ready to eat! Enjoy!

Tip: Add sliced chicken

 Gluten free

Cauliflower Rice Snack

Ingredients

Cauliflower (see recipe on page ??)
Sliced cucumber
Sliced cherry tomatoes
Sliced ham
Chopped bell peppers/paprika / capsicum

 Gluten free

Immune Boosting Soup

Ingredients

4,5 dl/ 1,9 cups of carrots, chopped
2,5 dl/ 1 cup of celery, chopped
2,5 dl/ 1 cup of leeks, chopped
2,5 dl/ 1 cup of yellow onions, cut in small bits
4 garlic cloves, chopped
2,5 dl/ 1 cup of chopped fresh parsley
1 Tablespoon fresh shredded ginger
2 Tablespoons of Basil, chopped
Himalayan salt
Pepper
2 Tablespoons of chopped chives for garnish
2 liters of water
Olive oil for cooking

This is how you do it:

Heat some olive oil in a big pot. Add the celery, carrots, chives, ginger, garlic, onions and sauté for 10 minutes over medium heat. Stir often.

Add the parsley and basil and 2 liters of water. Add salt and pepper. Turn up the heat until it boils and then let it simmer for 20 minutes with the lid on. Serve in a big bowl with chopped parsley as garnish.

Tip: Use this as a meal you can bring along with you in a thermos.

 Vegan  Vegetarian  Gluten free

Tomato Soup

Ingredients

500 grams of tomatoes, chopped
1 onion, chopped
1/2 fresh chopped chili or a pinch of chili powder
2 cans of tomatoes with basil and garlic
0,5 liter/ 16.9 ounces of vegetable stock
 Coconut oil/ olive oil
Taste to with Himalayan salt and pepper
2-3 hard boiled eggs cut in boats and added in as boats after the soup is done.

This is how we do it:

Sauté the onions, chili and the fresh tomatoes in olive oil, add the canned tomatoes and the vegetable stock and let it boil up for 15 minutes. Take the pot off the stove and use a hand blender to make an even soup. Add 3 Tablespoons of olive oil or coconut oil and taste to with pepper and Himalayan salt.

Vegan   Vegetarian

Winter soup

Serves 4

Ingredients

1 celeriac, cut into cubes
4 sweet potatoes, cut into cubes
4 yellow onions, chopped
1 dl (0,4 cups) of brown lentils
1 lemon, squeeze the juice and grate the peel
1 tbsp chopped fresh thyme or dried
1 tbsp cumin
5 tbsp coconut oil
1 vegetable stock
Himalayan salt to taste
Pepper to taste

This is how you do it:

Heat the chopped onion in 1 Tablespoons of coconut oil. Add in the veggies and pour water 2-3 cm/ 1-2 inches over it and let simmer down for 20 minutes after it has boiled up. Add the rest of the coconut oil towards the end. Add a pinch of Himalayan salt or more after taste.

 Vegan  Vegetarian Gluten free

Yummy Lentil Soup

Ingredients

500 grams red lentils
1 yellow onion, chopped
2 cloves garlic, minced
1 celeriac (celery root) chopped into cubes
10 cherry tomatoes, chopped in halves
1 leek
5 Tablespoons coconut oil (1 Tablespoon for sautéing)
1 vegetable stock
1 liter of water
Himalayan salt and pepper to taste

This is how you do it:

Cut up the vegetables and sauté the onion, garlic and celery root over medium heat. Don't let it get brown. Pour over water and add the stock. Rinse the lentils before you add them to the boiling water and let it simmer in about 12 minutes. Add in the tomatoes after 6 minutes and add the leek and the coconut oil towards the end and add Himalaya salt.

 Vegan  Vegetarian Gluten free

Dinners

Dinners

Salmon Salad

Pad Thai with Chicken

Chicken Bacon Tropic Dish

Filled Zucchini Boats

Sushi

Josh Rogan - Indian Lamb

Mini Pizzas

Taco Stuffed Bell Peppers

Ratatouille

Baked Salmon

Asian Chicken Soup

Sweet Potato Casserole with Bacon and Mushroom

 Vegan  Vegetarian  Gluten free

Salmon Salad

Ingredients

2 -3 big slices of salmon baked in coconut oil and garlic
        (see «Baked Salmon» recipe)
1/2 cucumber, chopped
1/2 bell pepper, julienned
1/2 can of pineapple and its juice
1/2 red juicy apple
Some halved cherry tomatoes
A small handful of pine nuts
A cup of green salad mix of choice
Himalayan salt to taste
Pepper to taste

This is how we do it:

Toss the greens together, add the pineapple juice and add the salmon in chunky pieces on top. Serve on plates. Voilà your dinner is ready to eat.

 Gluten free

Pad Thai with Chicken

Serves 4

Ingredients

3 Tablespoons coconut oil, for cooking
2 cloves garlic, minced
4 spring onions, diced
1 packet soft rice noodles
1 Tablespoon apple cider vinegar
2,5 Tablespoons maple syrup
Dash of Cayenne pepper
1 tin of bean sprouts
Vanessa's spice mix (optional)
2 medium sliced chicken breast
1 egg (optional)

For garnish:
A handful of pine nuts, roasted and crushed
1/2 teaspoon of red pepper flakes
1 lime, cut into boats

This is how you do it:

Put the noodles in warm water for about 6 minutes for them to soften up or follow the directions on the back of the package.
Heat the oil in a wok or large frying pan on medium heat. Add the garlic and half of the spring onions. Stir fry for 40 seconds. Whisk together the apple cider vinegar, maple syrup, coconut sugar, cayenne pepper in a bowl and add in to the pan. Add the rest of the spring onions. Stir fry for 2 minutes or until noodles are cooked.

In a separate pan cook the chicken with coconut oil, Himalayan salt and pepper or Vanessa's spice mix. Crack the eggs in a preheated pan and allow to fry for about a minute, then break it up with a spoon and add the onions and bean sprouts.

In the end toss it all together and serve with pine nuts, chili pepper flakes and lime boats.

 Gluten free

Chicken Bacon Tropic Dish

Serves 2 people

Ingredients

150 grams/ 5.3 ounces bacon chopped (tip: use a clean scissor)
2 chicken fillets sliced
2 onions chopped
1 garlic clove, minced
300 grams/ 10.6 ounces champignons / mushrooms cleaned and chopped
1/4- 1/2 can of pine apples, chopped
6-8 cherry tomatoes halved
Olive oil for cooking
1 can of coconut milk
1 vegetable stock
Chopped parsley

This is how we do it:

Cook the bacon until its crunchy and move it on to a plate. Cook the chicken separately as well. Heat up the pan and add olive oil. Add the garlic onions until it gets soft and transparent. Cook the mushrooms lightly by its own. Mix onions, mushrooms, pine apple and tomatoes add the coconut milk and crumble the vegetable stock into it. Add the chicken and the bacon and let it simmer for 5-6 minutes. Tip: This dish can be served with for example cauliflower rice, pasta or rice. I choose to not have extra carbs outside the vegetables in this recipe as it is quite filling.

 Gluten free

Filled Zucchini Boats

Serves 4

Ingredients

4 zucchinis
1 big yellow onion, sliced
1 can of peeled tomatoes
600 grams of minced meat of choice
100 grams champignons / mushrooms, sliced
2 cloves garlic, minced
Vanessa's spice mix (optional)

This is how you do it:

Cut the zucchinis in halves and dig out the middle, use a knife and a tea spoon. Brown the meat and the rest of the ingredients except for the zucchinis in a pan using some olive oil. Put the empty squashes in a oven-proof dish and fill them with the browned meat. Bake in the oven for 360F/180 C. Garnish with some chives.

Tip: Feel free to try with some non calcium vegan cheese

 Gluten free

Sushi

Serves 2 people

Ingredients

6-8 gluten free tortilla wraps
150 grams of raw salmon sliced into thin 1 inch thick slices
Chives, chopped
2 avocados, sliced into thin slices
1 mango chopped into cubes
1/2 cucumber sliced into cubes
Wasabi (optional)

This is how we do it:

Add a bit of every thing into the wrap, roll it together and eat! :)

Tip: If you want to eat it like sashimi, skip the wrap.

Josh Rogan - Indian Lamb

Serves 2

Ingredients

400 grams of boneless lamb
1 yellow onion
2 Tablespoons coconut oil
2 Tablespoons Indian curry red paste
1 can chopped, tomatoes in a tin
1 teaspoon coconut sugar (or normal sugar)
2 Tablespoons coconut oil for cooking

This is how we do it:

Cut the lamb into dices about 1.5 inch x 1.5 inch / 3x3 cm. Add the meat and the onion in a warm pan and with coconut oil. Add the curry paste when the onion has become brown. Add the tinned tomatoes and let everything simmer for 10-15 minutes. Stir inn the coconut sugar and the coconut oil.

Tip: Serve with some greens or a side salad and rice. Try the cauliflower rice recipe SEE PAGE?. Garnish with fresh coriander/cilantro if you like.

 Gluten free

Mini Pizzas

Serves 1-2

Ingredients

1 large sweet potato
Tomato paste
Low calcium vegan cheese (optional)
1 bell pepper/paprika/capsicum chopped
1 small can pine apple, chopped
1 can mushrooms, sliced
1/2 red onion chopped
1 garlic clove minced (optional)
Pepper to taste
Spice of choice (oregano is a favorite on pizza)

Other topping options:
Pepperoni/ pine nuts/spinach etc

This is how we do it:

Cut the sweet potato into a 1 inch/ 2 cm thick "flat boats" looking like a mattress. Put them in the oven for 5- 7 minutes. Take them out and add on the toppings putting the tomato paste as the first layer. Then put them into the oven again for another 10-15 minutes. Check with a fork for the consistency before you take it out. You might have to work to find a temperature and time that works better for your oven.

 Vegan  Vegetarian  Gluten free

Taco Stuffed Bell Peppers

Ingredients

6-8 medium bell peppers, washed, top cut off, seeds removed
1 pound minced meat/ 600 grams (preferably grass-fed)
2 Tablespoons olive or coconut oil
1 clove garlic, pressed
Pepper and Himalayan salt
1 yellow onion, chopped
2 Tablespoons of Terrific Taco Seasoning see page ??

This is how you do it:

Preheat oven to 175C / 350F. Cook the meat in butter/oil on the stove and sprinkle 2 Tablespoons of Terrific Taco Seasoning over it. Mix well. After a few minutes, add the finely chopped onions and garlic and leave to simmer until the meat is thoroughly cooked. Add in the water and allow to simmer for a few minutes more. If you want it stronger, taste to with more of the Terrific Taco Seasoning. Place bell peppers in an oven-safe pan. Spoon mixture into bell peppers. Cover and bake for 30 minutes or until bell peppers are soft. Serve immediately.

Tip: Serve with the avocado mash see page ??, the tomato salsa see page ??, corn, chopped cucumbers and low calcium vegan cheese

 Vegan  Vegetarian  Gluten free

Ratatouille

Serves 4

Ingredients

1 yellow onion, chopped
2 cloves garlic chopped
1 large zucchini sliced and halved
1 green bell pepper, chopped (capsicum/paprika)
1 red bell pepper, chopped (capsicum/paprika)
1 Tablespoon chili paste
Olive oil for cooking
2 cans of chopped tomatoes
1 vegetable stock (powder)
1 teaspoon basil
1 pinch of Himalayan salt

This is how we do it:

Cut, clean and chop all the ingredients (except from the spices). Add olive oil in a pan and sauté onion, garlic and chili in a few minutes on low heat.

Stir in zucchini, bell peppers, tomatoes and vegetable stock and let the dish simmer for about 20 minutes until the vegetables are soft. Add herbs and salt.

Tip: You can use carrots (thinly sliced) and leeks. You can also use chili paste instead of chili.

 Vegan    Vegetarian    Gluten free

Baked Salmon

Serves 2 people

Ingredients

4 nice pieces of salmon
1 big sweet potato
1 medium cauliflower
1 broccoli (optional)
Coconut oil or olive oil
Vanessa's spice mix (on the vegetables)
Himalayan salt, and pepper to taste
Lemon juice (optional, on the salmon)
Chopped up garlic (optional, on the salmon)
Basil (optional, on the salmon)

This is how we do it:

Cover a baking tray with parchment paper. Peel the sweet potato and cut into 1/2 inch / 1 cm thick rounds. Make place for the salmon in the middle that you will add later. Turn the oven to 400F/200C. Wash and cut up the cauliflower. Put the sweet potato and the chopped cauliflower on the baking tray, add some oil on each piece and sprinkle with Vanessa's spice mix. Turn the oven to 400F/200C and bake for about 10-15 minutes. Put some lemon juice, chopped up garlic, salt, pepper and optional basil on the salmon. Turn the oven down to 360F/180C and insert the salmon. Bake for another 15 minutes. Take out and enjoy!

Tip: If you don't want to eat 2 pieces of salmon then you can save one piece for the day after with a salad on the side, it tastes heavenly cold as well.

 Gluten free

Asian Chicken Soup

Serves 4

Ingredients

3 pieces of chicken breasts, sliced
8 dl/ 27 oz of chicken stock
100 grams of fresh grated ginger
1 garlic clove thinly sliced
1 lemon grass, chopped
2 Tablespoons Asian fish sauce
Juice and grating of 1 lime
4 dl/ 13,5 oz of coconut milk
4-8 Tablespoons coconut oil
Thinly sliced and chopped carrots (optional)
Chopped baby corn (optional)
Chopped bell peppers/paprika / capsicum

This is how we do it:

Boil up the chicken stock and add the ginger, garlic and lemon grass and let it simmer for 3 minutes. Add the chicken slices. Boil for another 2 minutes and add the rest of the ingredients. Add the coconut oil. Make sure that the chicken is finished before serving. Serve in soup bowls.

 Gluten free

Sweet Potato Casserole with Bacon and Mushroom

Serves 12

Ingredients

4,5 lbs / 2 kg of medium sweet potatoes
12 strips of bacon cut in small pieces.
4-6 big mushrooms sliced
1/2 onion chopped
3 tablespoons grass-fed organic butter
1 table spoon coconut oil, melted for coating baking dish
3-4 cloves of garlic
Himalayan salt
Pepper
1 tbsp cumin

This is how we do it:

Wash and peel the sweet potatoes. Slice them up and put them into a pot and boil. When they are so soft you can slide a fork through them without resistance then take them off the stove and sift out the water. Add all ingredients to the potatoes except the bacon, onions and the mushrooms and put it all in a food processor.
Cook up the bacon and onions and mushrooms separately and add into the mash when it is finished. Voila you have a delish dinner that if you make double or triple portions you can have dinners for the next days or freeze down for later.

 Gluten free

Desserts & Snacks

Desserts & Snacks

Spiced Up Muffins

Sweet Potato Waffles

Brownies with Pine Nuts

Date Snacks Balls

Sorbet

Homemade Chips

Mini Bounty Hearts

Puffed Chocolate Rice Cakes

Banana Bread

Nice Cream

 Vegan   Vegetarian   Gluten free

Spiced Up Muffins

Ingredients

150 grams/ 5.3 ounces of soft coconut oil/ grass fed butter
200 grams/ 7 ounces of coconut sugars
2 teaspoons of vanilla extract/powder/sugar
2 teaspoons of baking soda
4 eggs
3 dl any healthy gluten free flour that is low in calcium
2 teaspoons ground cinnamon
1 teaspoon of ground ginger
1/2 teaspoon of ground of clove
1/2 teaspoon of ground of cardamom
1/2 teaspoon of ground of all spice

This is how we do it:

Whisk butter/coconut oil, coconut sugar and vanilla sugar together. Add one and one egg and stir well between. Add the rest of the ingredients and stir well.
Pour into muffin forms and bake on 360F/180C for about 20 minutes plus minus, however, I would check on the way, they can take way less time depending on the oven.
Check the cake by sticking a stick or a fork to check when its finished.

 Vegan  Vegetarian Gluten free

Sweet Potato Waffles

Ingredients

2 medium - big sweet potatoes, peeled and shredded
2 big eggs
1/2 teaspoon of cinnamon
A dash vanilla sugar (optional)
A pinch of Himalayan salt
Coconut oil for the waffle maker

This is how you do it:

Mix the peeled and shredded sweet potatoes with the eggs, cinnamon, Himalayan salt and vanilla extract. Melt the fat on the waffle maker and cook the sweet potato waffle texture. Cook it until golden or when the waffle make says its finished.

 Vegan    Vegetarian   Gluten free

Brownies with Pine Nuts

Ingredients

100 grams / 3 1/4 ounces of pine nuts
100 grams/ 3 1/4 ounces of grass fed butter or coconut butter
150 grams of dairy free 70-86% dark chocolate
1 teaspoon black coffee
1 teaspoon vanilla extract
100 grams / 3.25 ounces of coconut flower sugar
4 eggs

This is how we do it

Grind the nuts. Melt chocolate and butter together over a water bath. Stir until the texture is all is smooth. Take it off the water bath and pour in the coffee and the vanilla powder/extract. Wait until it has cooled down.

Add in the pine nuts and the coconut sugars. Whisk the egg yolks together and add them in. Whisk the egg whites together until they are firm.

First take one big spoon of the egg whites in to the chocolate texture. Then add the rest until its nicely mixed.
Pour it all into a 20 cm by 20 cm cake form. Approximately 9x9 inch form. Use baking paper.

Put the cake in the oven on 180 C/360 F for 20-25 minutes until it is firm on the top but still soft in the middle.

Cut the cake into squares and cool it of in the baking form.

 Vegan  Vegetarian  Gluten free

Date Snacks Balls

Ingredients

12 small or 8 big dates
2 dl of shredded coconut
1 topped Tablespoon coconut oil
A pinch of Himalayan salt
A pinch of grounded ginger
A pinch of cinnamon
2 Tablespoons of lemon juice (optional)

This is how we do it:

Add everything into your food processor and let it run until smooth texture, form balls with a Tablespoon and your hand or put them in silicon forms such as I have done in the picture. Set them in the fridge for 20 minutes and they are ready to serve.

 Vegan  Vegetarian Gluten free

Orange Sorbet

Ingredients:

2 oranges, peeled
9,4 dl/ 4 cups ice

This is how we do it:

Place ingredients in a high-speed blender and blend for 1 minute or until you achieve an crushed ice consistency.

Tips: Add honey, maple syrup, vanilla extract, flavored stevias for sweeter or more taste.

For strawberry sorbet or mixed berries, replace the oranges with the one you want. E.g. 4,7 dl/ 2 cups strawberries or 4,7 dl/ 2 cups of mixed berries. Add oat or rice milk for a creamier taste.

Coconut Mango Sorbet

Ingredients

1 cup chopped peeled, frozen mango
3/4 cup coconut milk
1 teaspoon coconut sugar
A dash vanilla

This is how we do it:

Add together in a blender and serve

 Vegan  Vegetarian  Gluten free

Homemade Chips

Slice your favorite low calcium veggies or a combination of them put them in a zip lock bag with olive oil (or melted coconut oil) and with your favorite spices, let it sit for 15 minutes and then put on tray in the middle of the oven with parchment paper and let it bake. Depending on the vegetable, usually it takes between 15-25 minutes on 380 F/180 C.

 Vegan  Vegetarian Gluten free

Mini Bounty Hearts

About 18 pieces

Ingredients

160 grams shredded, unsweetened coconut
4-5 Tablespoons of Agave Syrup
2 Tablespoons Coconut Oil.
1/2 teaspoon vanilla extract
1/2 teaspoon of Himalaya salt
1-2 x 100 grams of dairy free 86 % dark chocolate

This is how we do it:

Put everything in a bowl, except from the dark chocolate. Mix all well together and put them in forms of your choice, I used heart shaped silicon forms.

Melt the dark chocolate with the coconut oil over a warm bath, this is how I do it:
Heat up water in your water boiler. Pour the water into a plastic bowl, then grab another smaller plastic bowl and place upon the water in the bigger plastic bowl. Then put the chocolate and the coconut oil in the small bowl and stir until it is melted.

Pour tiny bit of the chocolate melt in the heart forms, like 1/3 or 1/4 of the form. Then stick the form in the fridge for 20 minutes or until its stiff. Then take them out and add the coconut filling on top of it. Leave some room so you can seal them with the rest of the chocolate sauce. Put them back in the fridge and wait 30 minutes for them to get stiff. Push them gently out of their form and serve them cold. They will melt if you keep them out for a while so put them back in the fridge. You can also freeze them.

 Vegetarian  Gluten free

Puffed Chocolate Rice Cakes

Ingredients

250 grams of coconut oil
200 grams of dairy free 86% dark chocolate
2 eggs
2 dl coconut sugars
2 Tablespoons strong chocolate/espresso
100 grams of puffed rice

This is how we do it:

Melt the chocolate and coconut oil over low heat or use 2 plastic bowls on top of each other where the lower one is filled with hot water and the top one contains the chocolate and coconut oil. Let it cool down. Stir until fluid. Whisk eggs and sugars together. Add in the coffee, the chocolate and the puffed rice and mix together. Use spoons to make small cakes and put it on a parchment paper on top of a plate or in muffin/cup cake forms and put them in the fridge for 20 minutes. Can be stored in the freezer.

 Vegetarian   Gluten free

Banana Bread

Ingredients

5 eggs
225 grams of coconut oil
300 grams of coconut sugar
400 grams of any healthy gluten free flour that is low in calcium
2 teaspoons baking powder
1 1/2 teaspoons of baking soda
1 1/2 teaspoons of ginger (grounded)
1 1/2 teaspoons of cardamom
1 Tablespoon of cinnamon
5-6 bananas
1,5 dl / 5 ounces of hot water (use the water boiler)
A handful of pine nuts (optional)

This is how we do it:

Whisk eggs and coconut sugars together. Add all the rest of the dry ingredients. Melt coconut oil and blend it all together. Mash the bananas with a fork and pour the water over it. Add in some pine nuts if you like. Pour the batter in a buttered bread loaf pan. Bake at 350 F/ 175 C for about 30 mins. Check before the time with a fork as ovens are different in temperature.

Tip: Banana bread can also be baked as cupcakes and even frozen to last longer.

 Vegan  Vegetarian  Gluten free

Strawberry Nice Cream

Ingredients

2 frozen bananas
1 dl /1/2 cup frozen strawberries
1 teaspoon vanilla extract

This is how we do it:

Blend until smooth ice cream consistency in the food processor.
Add some fluids to get it smoother e.g. pine apple juice or oat milk.
If the consistency becomes too tight, add more liquid, if it gets too
loose add more frozen banana.

Vanilla Nice Cream

Ingredients

2 frozen bananas
1 teaspoon vanilla extract

This is how we do it:

Blend until smooth ice cream consistency in the food processor.
Add some fluids to get it smoother e.g. pine apple juice or oat milk.
If the consistency becomes too tight, add more liquid, if it gets too
loose add more frozen banana.

 Vegan  Vegetarian  Gluten free

Sides

Sides

Cauliflower Rice

Mashed Avocado

Red Bell Hummus

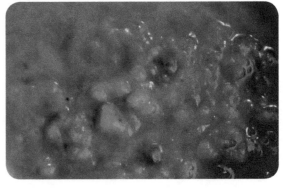

Tomato Salsa

 Vegan   Vegetarian   Gluten free

Cauliflower Rice

Serves 4

Ingredients

1 cauliflower
4 Tablespoons of pine nuts
Olive oil/ coconut oil for cooking
Pepper
Himalayan salt

This is how we do it:

Shred the cauliflower with a grater. Heat the frying pan and dry cook the pine nuts until they have got color but do not burn them. Warm olive oil in a pan and add the cauliflower "rice" and stir well. When the "rice" is warm, add the pine nuts and add Himalayan salt and pepper.

Tip: Make cauliflower rice, add some cherry tomatoes, pieces of ham or chicken and bring it with you in a snack box, ready to be eaten whenever you are.

 Vegan  Vegetarian Gluten free

Mashed Avocado

Serves 4

Ingredients

2 medium avocados, mashed flesh (stone removed)
1 medium clove garlic, minced
1 Tablespoon finely chopped coriander/cilantro
1/2 lime, juiced
Himalayan salt to taste
Pepper to taste

This is how we do it:

Mash together and serve on your plate

 Vegan  Vegetarian  Gluten free

Red Bell Hummus

Ingredients

2 red capsicums/red peppers cut in 2 halves
1 chili, remove the kernels
2 clove garlic cloves
Shredded lemon peel
Lemon juice from a lemon
1 Tablespoon olive oil

This is how we do it:

Grill the red bell peppers in the oven until the skin gets dark and peel it off. Put everything in a food processor and voila - red bell hummus.

 Vegan  Vegetarian Gluten free

Tomato Salsa

Ingredients

1/4 red pepper, in chunky pieces
1/4 red chili, in chunky pieces
1/4 red onion, in chunky pieces
1/2 box of canned tomatoes
1 teaspoon tomato purée
Fresh coriander/cilantro
3-4 Tablespoons of olive oil
1 / 2-1 lime, pressed
Himalayan salt
Pepper

This is how we do it:

Add peppers, chili, onions, tomatoes and tomato sauce in a food processor and let it run it until they are finely chopped.

Add olive oil until it gets a even consistency and taste to with lime juice, salt, pepper and coriander/cilantro. Let the salsa sit for a while before serving, in order for the good tastes to sink in.

 Vegan  Vegetarian Gluten free

Smoothies

Smoothies

Tropical Smoothie

Strawberry Ginger Green Smoothie

Christmas Smoothie

 Vegan   Vegetarian   Gluten free

Tropical Smoothie

Ingredients

1 frozen banana
1 juice of two passion fruits
1/2 a dragon fruit (optional)
1/2 cup / 1,2 dl pineapple
1/2 cup / 1,2 dl mango
1 tablespoon of vanilla protein powder in low calcium
1 cup / 2,4 dl of oat milk (organic, not calcium fortified)

This is how we do it:

Blend it together in a blender and serve straight away.

Tips: Make a double portion and freeze half the portion blended or unblended and use later.

 Vegan    Vegetarian   Gluten free

Strawberry Ginger Green Smoothie

Ingredients

2 cups/4,7 dl oat milk (organic, not calcium fortified)
1 cup/ 2,4 dl baby spinach/kale
1 cup/ 2,4 dl strawberries
1 1/2 frozen bananas
1 tbsp grated ginger, to taste
1 scoop vanilla protein powder (low calcium)

This is how we do it:

Add all the ingredients in the blender and serve cold and fresh

 Vegan  Vegetarian Gluten free

Christmas Smoothie

Ingredients

1 frozen banana
1 cup/ 2,4 dl water or oat milk (organic, not calcium fortified)
1 pinch Himalayan salt
1/4 teaspoons of clove
1/4 teaspoons of ginger
1/2 teaspoons of cinnamon
1 Tablespoon of Vanilla Protein Powder or other
low calcium protein powder or vanilla sugar/extract.

 Vegan  Vegetarian Gluten free

Mind, Exercise & Creativity

ONCE YOU CONQUER YOUR MIND, YOU CAN CONQUER ANYTHING.

www.outstandinghealth.fit

Dr. Coimbra on Stress Management

«We have in our brain stem cells which are cells that are multiplying and giving rise to new neurons, in a continuous process. This knowledge was established fairly recently, in 1998, leaving behind the old idea that nerve tissue does not have the capacity to recover, that the cells that we had from birth would be the maximum number of nerve cells that we would have for life, and that we could only loose cells and not form new ones.

Today, we know that we form new cells, and that the formation of new nerve cells depends on emotional stability. This is a fundamental basic factor. Constant stress, pain, anxiety and depression, are things that block the production of new brain cells and prevent the replacement of lost brain cells, promoting the ageing of the nerve tissue and setting the individual up to develop neuro degenerative diseases.»

– Dr Cicero Galli Coimbra

Mind, Soul & Body: Thoughts create and form your life

I believe we as human beings consist of being a spirit, having a soul (mind, will and emotions) and that we are living in a body.

Let's talk about soul, mind and body from a perspective of science, psychology and health.

«What you think matters because what you think creates matter»
– Dr Caroline Leaf, drleaf.com

«HEALTH ISN'T JUST ABOUT EXERCISING OR WHAT YOU ARE EATING. IT IS WHAT YOU ARE THINKING AND WHAT YOU ARE SAYING.»

«How you think about a problem is more important than the problem itself»

Mind

Daniel Kahneman, widely regarded as one of the worlds most influential living psychologist says that we essentially consist of two selves - our *experienced self* and our *remembered self* and that we do not make future decisions based on *experiences* but our *memories of experiences*. So our personal happiness is not rooted in our "*experienced self*" but in our "*remembered self*".

Even though painful experiences bring us great sorrows, our experiences will not be the dominant force affecting our personal happiness. It is our "remembered self" that

controls how we perceive and experience life.

The human brain is designed to relive the past experience when we remember it. Our brain seems incapable of distinguishing the «actual event» from the «remembered event». Inside the brain the memory and the experience is one and the same. How we translate life through experiences and choose to let go and move on, through forgiveness towards others and ourselves, is one of the key ingredients here.

«Not forgiving someone is like drinking poison and expecting the other person to die».

— Joyce Meyer

Erwin Raphael MCManus writes in his book "The Artisan Soul" «We are interpreters. This is the way we are designed. We are translators of meaning, and thus everything we see, hear, smell, touch, taste, and experience is processed through all our previous experiences and perceptions. We

don't see people for who they are; we see them through the filter of everyone we have ever known. We don't see circumstances as they are; we see them through the filter of everything we have ever experienced. No experience is an experience in isolation. Every experience is interpreted by the overarching story of our lives, and those experiences give us greater clarity».

He further writes «Our interpretation will be informed either by the worst of who we can be or by the best of what it means to be human. When we allow our filter to be shaped by bitterness and jealousy and envy and greed and hatred and apathy,

our interpretation of life is skewed and the future becomes smaller and smaller. It is here that our interpretation of life causes us to experience each day with doubt and apprehension. When our life is informed by the best of human emotions, when we are informed by love and hope and faith, it changes the way we see everything».

«If you realized the damage negative thoughts have on your mind, you would never think a negative thought again!»
— Dr. Caroline Leaf, drleaf.com

Trauma & toxic thoughts

Illness can come through the mind or soul such as trauma or toxic thinking. Science shows that 75-98 % of diseases come from toxic thinking, meaning how we think about life, stress, challenges and the choices we make based on our thinking. That means only 2 % of diseases are genetic. (Based on the book "Switch On Your Brain: The Key to Peak Happiness, Thinking, and Health" by cognitive neuroscientist Dr Caroline Leaf)

Trauma (a high level of emotional stress) is an attack on the brain that makes the body, at worst, attack itself. As mentioned before, we can also be genetic disposed to this kind of self-attack, by e.g. having defect vitamin D3 receptors like I have (based on the gene test I took)

But what is toxic thinking? Thoughts of jealousy, anger, bitterness, feeling like a victim of life, out-of-control, stress and abuse have been proven to make people ill. The same toxic thoughts, like jealously, anger bitterness etc, that make a person do harmful actions to other people like, in worst case murder or depriving another human being of forgiveness, are the same toxic

thoughts that when unresolved, kill your own body too. Interesting, right?

Science has shown that when we think these toxic thoughts the brain creates protein, it creates matter. This is called neuroplasticity, meaning your brain can be formed and changed by the information you give it.

have influence over us will never understand fully how their words help shaping us. Our internal voice begins as an echoing of the voices of others. Before we spoke for ourselves, somebody spoke on our behalf, before we declared who we were, our souls formed around the declarations of others saying who we were.

The soul

The soul is the non-material part in humans that reflects the divine in us that is designed to be shaped by our passions, experiences and values. The soul is made by impressionable material, it forms itself around what ever material is informing it. What informs us forms us. The people who

The internal narrative

This leads us to the questions: Who have you been listening to? Who's voice have you been following? What story are you telling yourself? Who's lies are dictating your soul?

You haven't come this far,
 to only come this far!

SOMETIME WHEN THINGS ARE FALLING APART THEY MAY ACTUALLY FALL INTO PLACE.

Exercise and Bone Density

A "selfie" of my feet
I took at the gym.

Exercise is very important and if you follow the Coimbra Protocol/High Dosing of Vitamin D3 then you need to exercise to avoid bone loss. People in wheelchair or who cannot exercise can take medications prescribed by their doctors.

Coimbra prescribes **Aerobic Exercises 3x or 5 x Per Week** (if possible) for **30 minutes**. It helps to release a substance from the thyroid that protects bone mass much better than vitamin K2. Moreover, it also helps to

create new brain cells, which is called neuro genesis. Weight training is also important for creating Human Growth Hormones and bone density.

Should you take K2?

Dr. Coimbra tells his patients that they can take vitamin K2 if they want, but they should NOT expect it to protect their bones or kidneys, even if taken in high doses. It seems to have no proven effect.

Magnesium

Magnesium is an **antagonist** of calcium. Therefore magnesium also helps protecting the bones. Vitamin D3, Magnesium and exercise are the key – so you better start to move and exercise.

Never too old for exercise!

You are never too old to work out, **Ernestine Shepherd** who is the oldest female body builder at 80 years old, she started training when she was 56! Search on YouTube to see some inspirational videos of her.

Photo: ernestineshepherd.net

Ernestine Shepherd started training at 56

Starting Cardio Exercises:
5 Days a Week Plan - Week 1

Day 1

10 min
Moderate intensity

Treadmill, bike, elliptical, brisk walk, rowing machine, swimming (or a combination)

Stretch

Day 2

15 min
Moderate intensity

Treadmill, bike, elliptical, brisk walk, rowing machine, swimming (or a combination)

Stretch

Day 3

20 min
Moderate intensity

Treadmill, bike, elliptical, brisk walk, rowing machine, swimming (or a combination)

Stretch

Day 4

25 min
Moderate intensity

Treadmill, bike, elliptical, brisk walk, rowing machine, swimming (or a combination)

Stretch

Day 5

25 min
Moderate intensity

Treadmill, bike, elliptical, brisk walk, rowing machine, swimming (or a combination)

Stretch

Starting Cardio Exercises:
5 Days a Week Plan - Week 2

Day 1

20 min
Moderate intensity or push yourself if your form allows it.

Treadmill, bike, elliptical, brisk walk, rowing machine, swimming (or a combination)

Stretch

Day 2

25 min
Moderate intensity

Treadmill, bike, elliptical, brisk walk, rowing machine, swimming (or a combination)

Stretch

Day 3

25 min
Moderate intensity or push yourself if your form allows it.

Treadmill, bike, elliptical, brisk walk, rowing machine, swimming (or a combination)

Stretch

Day 4

30 min
Moderate intensity

Treadmill, bike, elliptical, brisk walk, rowing machine, swimming (or a combination)

Stretch

Day 5

30 min
Moderate intensity or push
yourself if your form allows it.

Treadmill, bike, elliptical, brisk
walk, rowing machine, swimming (or a combination)

Stretch

KEEP AT IT, YOU DON'T SEE IT YET, BUT YOU WILL.

Art and Creating is a Key Part of a Healthy Life

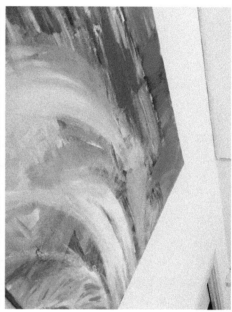

Some paintings I'm working on.

Creating is all about identity. We create from who we are. Art is about healing and the brain creating new structures, new paths and new brain cells. Art is creativity in its finest form. – It's a spiritual healing journey.

I have experienced that God uses art to pass people's minds and I can tap into a source bigger than myself where I can draw out healing for myself and others. The hands manifest only what my mind creates. It is like occupying two territories at the same time, Heaven and Earth.

Live Fully Right Where You Are» that «Joy is the realest reality, the fullest life, and joy is always given, never grasped» and this is how I feel when I create out of inspiration. Further she writes that «The whole of life even the hard is made up of the minutes parts, and if I miss the infinitesimals, I miss the whole».

Sometimes we miss the small minutes of what really matters and those moments that

Some of the crystal
earrings I have
designed by hand

make it all complete. Creativity
is to create time out of the
busy auto pilot schedule our
minds usually are set on in our
busy daily lives, and step into
another dimension of joy and
living, not just existing.

My creative journey started with God. With
that little voice and those big enfolding
visions. Because we co-create with the
invisible when we are imagining with our
minds. It is like child's play - we can imagine
a life we have never lived.

So when all of my thinking has been shaped
as a result of being in pain, having fatigue,

been isolated - I choose to break that
thought pattern by looking for new life giving
thoughts, painting another dream or creating
jewelry.

It is in those moments that I know I am more
than a body, more than a mind and more
than just a human being. In those moments
I am art, I am creativity, I am joy and I am
whole. I express my identity, my truest self
and I materialize it.

To me colorful crystals are a reminder of the colorful beauty of Heaven and God's love and inspiring presence.

My journey started about 10 years ago with the sudden need to create jewellery and I used my lunch break at work doing it. I was just very fascinated.

One day a lady at church wanted me to make her some jewellery. I had to meet her at another prayer house to deliver them to her. I came before she was finished with her singing session. While waiting for her I was

Silver charms and crystals earrings called Galla Cherubs with a golden charms and crystals necklace.

Dress: Kathrine Nørgård, kathrinenorgard.no
Photo: Rodrigo Reyes, powerportraits.net
Model: Donna-Linn Krogsund Mella

Official promotion picture for the Norwegian edition of «Dancing with the Stars 2012» on TV 2 with the contestants wearing my jewelery.

The Norwegian Miss World 2012 contestant wearing my jewelery

Taking and editing colorful photos can also be a creative healing experience for me.

drawn into the presence of God's Spirit and the prophetic music.

Long story short that became my spiritual resting place for the next two years. While just being there I experienced God's healing in many places in the deepest deep of my soul. I also saw many designs in the spirit of jewellery and my creativity was endless.

Not much later my jewellery was to be seen in the high end fashion boutiques of Oslo, the capitol of Norway. Also on celebrities, and representatives of the Royal Family such as the daughter of the Norwegian

King himself. The jewellery was also a main sponsor for the Miss World Norway 2012 and was seen on the Norwegian contestant in China by over 50 million people worldwide.

This sounds like a great story of success, but like I wrote elsewhere, I have been fighting fatigue and sickness for too many years and my art is part of the ongoing healing process. It is an important part that I'm constantly revisiting whether I am able to sell it or not.

Creating art is healing for me and can bring healing to others too. Try it for yourself!

Some photos I took on my iPhone
around Sandvika, Norway

Testimonies

Vitamin D3 against Crohns:

Chimene's Story

Chimene Schuster started on the Coimbra protocol to treat Crohns disease in April 2016 and by July it went into remission. When she started out she made several dose adjustments. Her improvement towards remission was however gradually, each day a novelty.

At the beginning of the treatment she had many doubts, she did not fully believe in the treatment. Gradually seeing her improvements she was getting more confident, and today she tells the news to everyone and spreads her success with the treatment.

Her life changed completely, mood, well-being, complete joy without any symptoms of the disease.

Today she is a new girl, full of life, and doesn't take any immunosuppressive drugs. She attributes her success to Vitamin D3 supplement and diet changes.

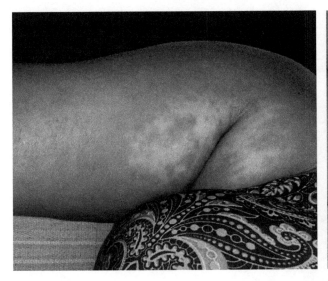
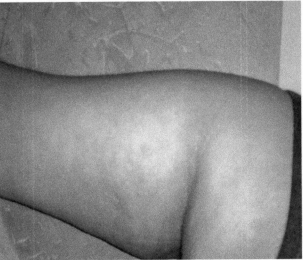

Vitamin D3 against Atopic Dermatitis: Gabrielle's story

Hello, my name is Gabrielle. I am 28 years old but was diagnosed with Atopic Dermatitis at the age of 18. The disease manifested with itching and dryness of the skin, mainly on the hands and knees. So the treatment I received was corticosteroids.

In 2015 I had another outbreak of the disease, but the medicine did not have any effect on me and as time passed I became worse, only this time around the disease manifested itself with a redness and itching all over my skin. And I was always cold. The disease became severe and by the end of 2016 I was not able to walk because of swelling in the joints.

As corticosteroids did not work, I experimented with the combination of an immunosuppressant and a corticosteroid to see if I could get any relief. At first I saw improvement, however, after one month of treatment I began to get worse again. I was hopeless, until the day my mother was looking on the Internet for reports similar to mine and came across the Coimbra Protocol.

After reading several favorable testimonials, we decided to try the protocol. It was my last hope. I made an appointment with one of the protocol doctors and started the treatment.

The improvement was visible on my skin in just two days! It has been a month and a half since I started the protocol. I realized my skin has become firmer and the redness is fading. I also no longer feel cold. I can testify that the Coimbra Protocol saved my life.

Before

Hormonal spots disappeared with Vitamin D3: Vanessa's Story

Only 5000 iu of vitamin D3 a day were enough to remove these hormonal/age spots when I started taking vitamin D3 supplements a bit over 5 years ago. The image on the top-left shows where I had the spots and the other images are from this year. They never returned, not even when I am out in the sun.

Vanessa Raphael

Vitamin D3 against Endometriosis and MS: Dora's Story

Hi! I'm Dora, immigrant from Russia to Argentina, to the very hot part of Argentina. Some people say that immigration is a big stressor for the body like MS. No, not if the body has good support and treatment. And the best MS treatment I found here, in Argentina.

My MS started in the very beginning of 2014 with nystagmus. Nobody told me to find out about this word on Internet or to find a neurologist because it was something neurological. It just passed and in 2 months started something new - a facial paralysis. It was severe. I couldn't feel the taste of food, couldn't look to the right side and couldn't smile. Then I went to the neurologist and he asked me to do MRI. But the result of MRI didn't show any answer to my questions

neither to that neurologist, nor to another one.

Four months passed and my symptoms went away until the end of the year when something more severe appeared. I couldn't walk alone. I could walk but it was impossible to take the correct direction. And then I got the PPMS diagnosis and prescription for Rebif. I don't want to describe my awful one-year-injection-experience, it basically just did not work and my lesions tripled. They offered me an MS medication called Gilenya. I read much about it and I just did not want it. I felt that there was something I was missing. And then I found the vitamin D3 option.

When I was doing my ultra sound before

starting the protocol, the doctor found a cyst in my right ovary. She advised me to go to the gynecologist and do the gynecological ultra sound. As a result of it, they found the cyst was very large and incurable except through surgery, so I had the surgery. The biopsy said without doubts it was Endometriosis, auto immune, chronic and which was going to return.

So returning to my vitamin D3 treatment, I just tried it waiting to receive my Gilenya. Within just one month it worked so well for me that I didn't try that poisonous pill. Vitamin D3 took away all of my symptoms very fast, at least 99% of them. But the 1% is still waiting to recover.

It does not mean that I have cured my MS, it can remind me its still there but those reminders are very subtle. The year 2014

I just remember as a nightmare where I learned knitting and fishing so I would not go crazy. More than one and a half years have passed now and the Endometriosis no longer bothers me. So I am healthy, active and want a baby, or two, or three...

Vitamin D3 against Fibromyalgia, Myofascial Pain Syndrome, Sjogren's Syndrome, IBS:

Hileia's Story

My name is Hileia Silva, I'm 52 years old. For many years I have been suffering from Fibromyalgia, Myofascial Pain Syndrome, Sjogren's Syndrome, severe depression, hypertension, asthma, chronic Colitis, inflammatory bowel disease, repeated urinary infections, Osteopenia, spinal and joint problems, kidney stones, gliosis and more. I have been through many doctors all my life but they have never given me hope. They only prescribed antidepressants, strong analgesics, muscle relaxants, anti-inflammatories, corticoids, blood pressure medications, etc and still I suffered the side effects of the medicines.

Two years ago I found the videos of Dr.

Cícero on the Internet talking about the Coimbra Protocol. On October 14, 2015 I met Dr. André Monteiro and Elaine Galhardo. I was so frail, weak and exhausted that I almost cried the whole appointment. They introduced me to the Protocol, welcomed me, changed my life because they gave me the hope of living better days!

I am gradually improving and the symptoms of each disease are disappearing. I no longer have symptoms of Fibromyalgia, Myofascial Pain Syndrome, or Sjogren's Syndrome. Depression and blood pressure are controlled without medication. I have had no further asthma attacks, Colitis, UTI's, or kidney stones. Osteopenia is gone, along

with the pain in spine and joints improved 90% despite still having degeneration of the joints.

My memory and concentration have improved greatly as well. Today I do not take any more medicine, just the supplements that are part of the Coimbra Protocol. From now on I am sure that I will continue to improve and be able to deal with the struggles and difficulties that arise and the ability to take care of myself and my family. I only have to thank God for the life of Dr. Cícero Coimbra who did not give up on this protocol and, as he himself says, "I put myself in the patient's place" and gave me the chance to live with dignity, renewing my hope. Immense and eternal gratitude to Dr. André Monteiro and Elaine Galhardo for accompanying me with all love.

Vitamin D3 against MS, Hashimoto's, Asthma:

Marija's Story

"When you get healed, spread the word." Is the meme I had in mind when the author of this book ask me to share my story with you.

I'm Marija Jillings, 40 years old, living in the Netherlands. I have MS, Hashimoto's, Asthma, and have been obese most of my life. My first Hashimoto's symptom started in 2013, shortly after an out of uterus pregnancy. I started thyroid medication to keep it under control as it is crucial for a successful pregnancy in the future.

At 37 I gave birth to a perfect, healthy baby boy. Unfortunately, shortly after the birth, I developed MS with symptoms of worsening vision, knee pain, chronic fatigue, and lack of libido. I have seen numerous neurologists that talked of MS but still I have no official diagnosis. The neurologist I see now believes it is MS but was told it would take a few years for an official diagnosis. Even so the neurologist was eager to start me on MS medication.

Before this time in my life, I never really knew what MS was or what MS medication can do to you. If it was not for breastfeeding, I probably would have taken the medication because who does not want to be well. But my situation was different, I never had a

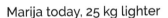
Marija today, 25 kg lighter

relapse and was told by one neurologist that I had PPMS so the medication for RRMS would not have helped.

My symptoms worsened with each passing day. Doctors blamed it on pregnancy hormones and were not helpful. As symptoms increased, I started dragging my left foot and had fears of dropping my 6 month old baby. At this point I got angry and threatened my doctor with placing explosives in her office if she would not give me a referral for an MRI! Which I then got. (Never underestimate the power of an angry pregnant woman!).

I did the MRI and then a week later an MRI with contrast, it all took so long. My sister asked if I was scared. I answered, "No, if it was something bad I would be dead by now." When I was young, I lost both parents to Cancer, so in my house "something bad" is Cancer. Little did I know that living with MS was no picnic either.

My MRI showed lesions but after 2.5 years I still had no diagnosis of MS. My good friend from high school has had MS for 16 years so she was the first person I contacted when I discovered MS symptoms. She told me about the high dose vitamin D3 treatment based on Dr. Coimbra from Brazil. Adding me to the Facebook group from our region, I started researching in the summer of 2016. I read many testimonies and realized I was blessed to have found this treatment at an early stage and the sooner I started the better chance for a "normal " life. All

Marija before

four conditions could be helped with this treatment so I made my decision quickly.

In January of 2017, I started the Coimbra Protocol under the supervision of protocol certified neurologist from Serbia, Dr. Bosnjak.

As of today I have been on the protocol 14 months. On my last annual MRI, it was discovered I had no new lesions, the MS progression has stopped. I no longer drag my foot, my libido has increased by about 80%, my eyes are improving, and I generally feel no fatigue or pain. I used to take my Asthma medication 4 times a day, now only once every other day.

Last year I avoided the flu, and my toddler attends daycare! My Hashimoto's results are very impressive as my antibodies have been reduced by more than 75% and for the last 5 years they were always way out of range.

And the last benefit, but definitely not the least, is I am no longer obese. I am still overweight but in the first year of the protocol I lost 25 kg (55 pounds)! No strict diet, just eliminating dairy and drinking 2.6 liters of water daily, requirements of the CP, also I removed all refined sugar and added lots of fruits and vegetables.

My life now is not "normal ", and it might never be again, but I have experienced so many benefits with the CP.

Today I thank Dr. Coimbra and Dr. Bosnjak for living a life knowing it might not be perfect, but it will not be worse, and with that hope, in time will even be better. They have given me the strength and courage to try for a second child, to bless my son with a sibling and my husband with another child. It might happen, it might not, but I can move ahead with the certainty that I will be fine afterwards.

EVERY TIME YOU
DRINK AND EAT YOU ARE
EITHER FEEDING A DISEASE
OR CURING IT.

www.outstandinghealth.fit

233

Vitamin D3 Reverses 24 Year History of MS:

Michael's Story

Michael Cawley is a MS patient turned Coimbra Protocol Specialist. Here is his story in his own words:

I had my first MS event in 1991 when I started to experience the intermittent loss of use of my left arm. In 1996 I had optic neuritis and lost the vision in my right eye for five days.

In 1998 I was on vacation in Orlando Florida and after three days sunbathing I noticed the electric shocks in my scalp disappeared.

I knew this improvement was somehow related to Vitamin D3. When I returned to Ireland within a few days the electric shocks returned. I visited my local health shop and purchased a bottle of 60 capsules of Vitamin D 400 iu each.

Slowly I began swallowing the capsules one at a time. After 30 capsules the electric shocks stopped. From that day onwards I consumed 12,000 iu of Vitamin D3 per day.

In 1999 onwards my symptoms became 24 /7 and I was experiencing hell on earth until January 2015 when I discovered the work of neurologist Cicero Galli Coimbra on YouTube. Following his advice I slowly improved and used Vitamin D3 on myself and other people who came to see me. So eventually I simply sent an email to this man who saved my life without charging me a dollar to say Thank You. He replied and learned I was using his approach on people here In Ireland.

He then offered to teach me free of charge for a week and he would not let me buy him lunch throughout that week. He is a lovely man to be in the presence of.

My GP was very concerned about the doses of Vitamin D3 but as he saw the shocking state of my health, he agreed to do calcium and kidney function blood tests so long as the blood results indicated my kidneys were safe.

Upon realising that the risk of kidney damage or even failure could be avoided by not drinking milk, or eating cheese or yogurt and by drinking 2.6 litres of fluids per day, I began taking whatever dose of Vitamin D3 made me feel the best which in my case was 100,000 iu per day (2.5 mg) and large amounts of liquid magnesium chloride. One of my symptoms was this horrible

heavy feeling like a lead cape draped over my body. Every movement required great effort and was totally exhausting. This feeling was always accompanied with a sense of disorientation like been hit by a concussion wave from an explosion and been thrown fifty yards through the air against a wall.

This symptom started to ease within 24 hours of my first 100,000 iu dose. Within a month so many improvements occurred that I became euphoric. It was like been hooked up to an I.V. and been drip fed life. Within six months I was a functioning human being once again.

Today I can drink alcohol (in moderation) eat most foods (except too much wheat), go for long walks and enjoy a normal life.

Unfortunate Side Effects of Steroid Treatment against MS: Helena's Story

Hi my name is Helena Kottovà, I live in the Czech Republic and have been an MS patient for six years.

It was my 21st birthday, I woke up and could not feel my entire right arm. So, on my birthday, I was at the hospital getting a CT and MRI. They told me there were some abnormalities on my tests and it could be cancer or maybe something else. For the next month my arm was numb but I was still going to work, writing at the local newspaper, and under a lot of stress. After a spinal tap later that month, they figured out it was MS.

They put me on Solumedrol steroid infusions. After two months of infusions they switched me to Prednisone in low doses. A few months passed and I started having breathing problems so I went off Prednisone. That is when hell broke loose... I had been through steroid withdrawal and red skin syndrome. It was terrible, real purgatory. My eyes were swollen every day and sometimes I could not open them. My skin was always red and swollen, so bad that even clothing was painful.

I quit my job, well I was fired, and stopped going out except to visit the doctors. Every time I went to the hospital they would put me on more steroids. One day, when I was home with my mum, I was having trouble breathing because my skin was in such bad condition. I really learned in those times that our skin is the biggest organ in our bodies.

My skin was bleeding. I had lost my hair, eyelashes, eyebrows, nails, and then my life. And what about the doctors here at the MS Center? Maybe they thought this was all very easy for me! The next treatment they suggested was Betaferon. I took that for two months until I got a bad skin infection for which I had several surgeries for skin

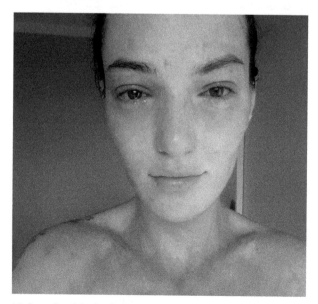

Helena's skin before

abscesses, severe depression, and flu-like symptoms. Next was Copaxone, which caused more hair loss and injection site pain. Then Tecfidera, definitely the worst, causing swelling and bringing back everything I had been through with the steroids.

Helena and her husband showing off her skin today.

Because of crying and not being able to live a normal life, I lost my job and two relationships. Then the medicines and careless doctors took three more years of my life. Until I said to myself, "I do not want my life to look like this!"

I stopped taking all the medicines including steroids, antihistamines, sleeping pills, pain killers, and MS drugs. My body started to heal very slowly and my journey had begun. I started to use only natural things like herbs and marijuana for my intense insomnia, because if you sleep only two hours a night you are willing to try anything... but that's a whole other book!

After five years of my disease I was in pretty good shape and heard about the Coimbra Protocol from a friend. She said she feels really good on high doses of vitamin D3.

So I went to Vienna with my husband and another friend that had MS, to meet Dr Blab, a protocol doctor. He started me on 50,000iu daily but I did not feel well on that dose so he lowered it to 20,000iu every day.

Now I have no more eczema or rashes, and my allergies are almost gone too. My MS is stable as my new MRI shows no new lesions.

I am still using herbs and nature based supplements etc. I have also found very nice doctors here and after six years of MS I have done something good for myself. I am now happily married to a good man for a year already, and trying to listen really well to my body. Living in peace, with my loving animals and understanding the exclusivity of that miracle that we all call life. :)

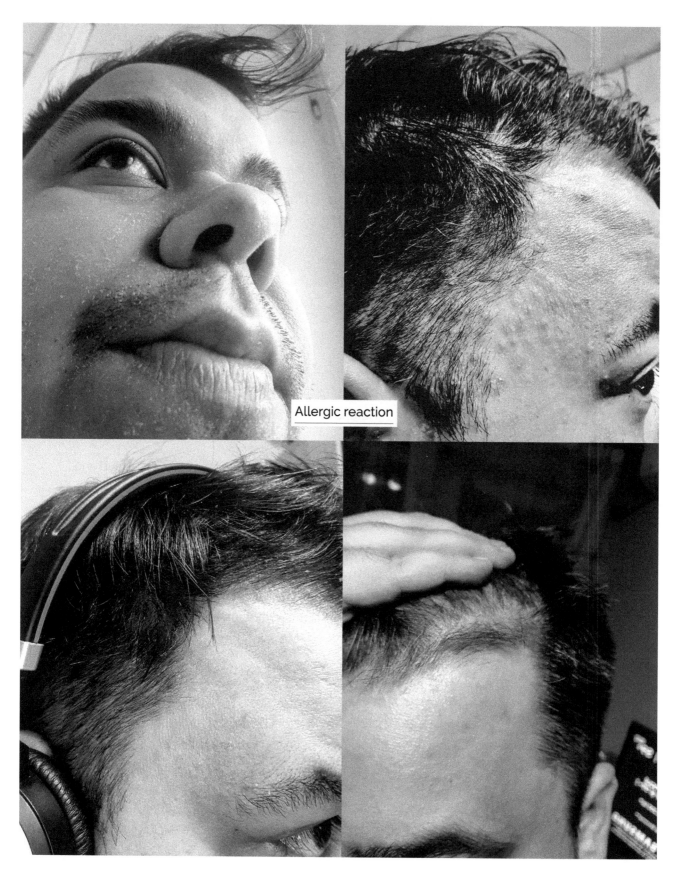

Allergic reaction

Not all supplements are created equal:

Eduard's Story

Eduard is a patient on the Coimbra Protocol using a less pure magnesium. He also used a too high dose of vitamin D3. Together it caused an allergic reaction. As you can see from the image the patient has an allergic reaction on his skin.

The two other images are taken two days after he stopped taking the magnesium. He also lowered his vitamin D3 dose.

This is why having a doctor to treat you and using pure minerals are important.

You can read about pure magnesiums on the website Vitamindlifestyle.com at this direct link https://vitamindlifestyle.com/the-miracle-and-importance-with-magnesium-on-the-coimbra-protocol/

Corrected Treatment and Dose Adjustments:

Adelina's Story

I am Adelina and I have been diagnosed with MS six months ago. I started the Coimbra Protocol in March 2018 and I was doing well in the first couple of days but as days went by my legs started feeling weaker and heavier by the day.

When I tried to contact my first Protocol Doctor via email it took days for him to reply but what was unacceptable to me is the fact that he told me it's ok to get worse in the beginning of CP because your body needs to get used to D3. Honestly I wasn't really sure how much worse was I willing to get in order to get better. So in a deep despair I contacted a different Coimbra Protocol Specialist and that's the best decision I have ever made.

My two main problems were walking properly and controlling my bladder. These two problems have been going on for more than a year.

My urinary urgency for two years now was a problem that has caused me a lot of stress. I had to visit the toilet every 15-20 minutes. Now it is getting better and better since I don't have to go to the toilet as often anymore. Now I go every 1-2 hours and it does not feel as urgent anymore.

I had been taking 60,000 iu of vitamin D3 per day for 20 days but my legs were getting much worse and the urinary control too. My new Coimbra Protocol Specialist suggested me to stop riboflavin and I felt a little better. It seemed that my body was having trouble converting Vitamin D3 and that the dose needed to be reduced. But when I reduced the dose of Vitamin D3 to 30,000 iu my legs started to feel like they were burning they got even weaker.

The following day he suggested me to take 80,000 iu and after doing so I felt an instant

improvement in energy and leg strength. My walking has improved too. I could not walk for more than 5 minutes without having to stop and rest because my legs felt so heavy and tired I could barely make another step. Now I can walk a lot more without having to stop and rest. Last weekend I traveled to Budapest where I had a great time! I was able to climb more than 500 stairs in order to reach the top of the biggest attraction in Budapest which is the Buda castle. I felt so happy to be able to do that. I guess I found what works best for me thanks to the wonderful Coimbra Protocol Specialist.

Corrected Treatment and Dose Adjustments:

Alina's Story

One Year on The Coimbra Protocol Without Benefit – Then Great Improvements after 4 Months With A Corrected Treatment and Adjusted Dose

I want to share with you my MS story, but most importantly, the remarkable progress the last four months. In July 2015 (Age 33) I had a MRI as I started to have numbness in my feet, and strange feelings in my abdomen, later identified as the MS hug. The result was indicating Multiple Sclerosis, but had to be confirmed by other investigations. And so, began the worst hospital experience of my life, with cortisol administration which gave me horrible side effects, and 5 spinal taps (first 4 were unsuccessful) made one after the other that left me almost unconscious, with no anesthetics. Weeks of tremendous pain and pure agony followed when MS symptoms aggravated combined with the terrible side effects of hospital treatment.

I had: extreme dizziness/vertigo, unbearable L'Hermitte sign, numbness and burning sensations on multiple parts of my body, an extremely intense MS hug, tinnitus, insomnia, anxiety, fatigue and brain fog. For two years, I was completely unable to work, my career completely stopped (I am a painter and an illustrator). I had to keep my head straight with my hands all the time, including while being on the street, trying to avoid the terrible dizziness (I wore the neck collar until I couldn't stand it anymore). I refused all the classic treatment that the neurologists wanted to prescribe me by knowing that my body would not sustain it and because I did not believe in it either.

Months after months I searched for some other totally different approach to MS on the Internet until the day I discovered the Coimbra Protocol. It sounded miraculous to me, powerful and completely logical in all its depth. In July 2016, a year after my diagnosis, I started the CP with great enthusiasm, under the supervision of my initial Coimbra trained Protocol Doctor. During a year of daily 60.000 units of vitamin D3 and numerous supplements (brands chosen by me after internet reviews, as no certain brands were pointed out), I noticed only small improvements, my major symptoms, dizziness, L'hermitte sign, MS hug, remained the same. Unbearable.

Because of a Facebook group I noticed the observations of a different Coimbra Protocol Specialist based in Ireland. I decided to seek a second opinion for my case. My first appointment was in July 2017 and he determined that 60,000 iu may be too much and might be triggering MS symptoms.

I followed his advice and within days started to feel a little better. Then week by week the symptoms all became less intense and overwhelming. Slowly I started believing in my body's ability to be heal again.
After four months treatment, I feel whole and normal, the dizziness, L'Hermitte sign, numbness, insomnia and anxiety are completely gone! I am back at my easel, working 8-9 hours a day. I cried with happiness the first day I realized that I woke up in a hurry, did all my morning routine and started working, without my brain sensing any discomfort at all... What made these huge improvements possible is my personalized treatment, the high-quality supplements I take, as I understood, brands tested by the Protocol Specialist on his own for a decade fighting his own MS. I have very close supervision of my daily doses of basically everything, based on the response of my body to each of them.

Today my MS is turned off by a combination of Vitamin D3 drops, Micellized Vitamin D3, pre activated B2, three separate types of Magnesium, DHA, Selenium, zinc and Vitamin K. If I take only normal Vitamin D3 all the MS symptoms will return. If I sunbathe and forget to reduce my vitamin D3 by 15,000 iu all of the MS symptoms return and I am a wreck all over again.

There is also a great help in my recovery, a detox product that my Protocol Specialist uses for himself and his patients, from all the heavy metals that accumulate in the body over time. These neuro toxic substances mimic MS symptoms and interfere with the metabolism of vitamin D3. I started this product just one month ago. This helped enormously with my brain fog, anxiety, intractable teeth pain and gave me a fantastic feeling of lightness. (In the first stages, my body reacted through fatigue and nausea, indicating the high levels of toxicity in my body). Now I continue with the PectaClear weekly.

DISCLAIMER::

Corrected Treatment and Dose Adjustments:

Sheila's Story

After I started on the Coimbra Protocol I found that I could not absorb ionic magnesium as within an hour of taking the capsule I would get palpitations and feel really unwell. Then I found the magnesium citrate, apart from loose stools, made me feel really sick all the time and not right. I also found the riboflavin B2 made the MS symptoms worse.

My Coimbra Protocol Specialist told me to drop my vitamin D3 down from 48,000iu to 34,000iu a day as I wasn't absorbing enough magnesium. I could only take neural magtein. I was disappointed but he put me on PectaClear to clear my body of heavy metals, etc. Later PectaSol was added to this also.

After about two months I tried magnesium citrate and it was fine. Then I tried the ionic magnesium, which had a really bad reaction for me, and that was fine. After a few days I tried the riboflavin and my body accepted that too.

This meant that I could now go back up with the D3 and back into the protocol. Without this intervention and taking PectaClear I would have had to give up my vitamin D3 protocol. I am so grateful to my Coimbra Protocol Specialist for keeping me on the protocol.

I am in my seventh month now from starting the CP and I am feeling really well. I have regained some of the movement in my fingers and legs which is more than I could have hoped for having MS over 40 years.

Corrected Treatment and Dose Adjustments:

Debbie's Story

I started on the CP in May of 2017 and did so well for the first 3 months! My IBS-D disappeared after 2 months on 25K iu of vitamin D3. Then, in September I was bumped up to 75K iu of vitamin D3 a day and was told to add one 50K iu powder pill a day. I was actually removed from the original magnesium multiple dosage/types I was on and was put on just 2 pills a day. I was also put on R5P, a type of pre activated riboflavin.

By late October, I was having horrible bone pain. It was so bad I was literally about to go ask for an alternative painkiller that mimic morphine because I knew Percocet would not cut it! I reached out to my Coimbra Protocol Specialist and all of a sudden I found they had stopped answering the phone and I could not connect with him! Later - I did actually find an email from his office but it was 7 or more days later and I was traveling for my sons wedding so I completely missed it. I had already realized that unless I shelled out $250 USD for an appointment - I wasn't getting anything!

His protocol suggestions are what was causing the issues and he gave me no further support! I was forced to quit exercising to keep the pain under control. Every. Single. Time. I exercised - I wanted painkillers! Ugh! In December, I ended up having an emergency appendectomy and my eating and electrolytes got off - so combined with the terrible (and unnecessarily expensive) supplements I was on, my hair started falling out and my nails began to break off in the quick and bleed (this is very painful by the way).

In January I reached out again to my protocol doctor and same results. I was literally told the he would address everything at our next paid appointment!!! Well, by this time I was fed up with the for-profit tactics (14 tubes of blood for check ups!!!) I was sent to their own 'pharmacy' to purchase supplements and not addressing issues/adjusting protocol for me without paying ($250 USD) every time I spoke to him!

I contacted a different Coimbra Protocol Specialist in February in lieu of my appointment with my first Coimbra Protocol Doctor and the new Protocol Specialist immediately sent me a new protocol worksheet and I started on his recommended supplements right away! I didn't even pay or see him till our March 2nd appointment, but he addressed me and helped me immediately. I get so much more support!!!

Now, my hair is not falling out anymore and I look like a porcupine with new hair growth! My nails are harder than they have ever been! I am confident I will continue to see better improvements!! Woohoo!

DISCLAIMER::
This article is not intended to provide diagnosis, treatment or medical advice. Content provided in this article is for informational purposes only. Please consult with a trained Protocol Coimbra Specialist regarding any diagnosis or treatment options. Information in this article should not be considered as a substitute for advice from trained Coimbra Protocol Specialist. The claims made about specific products throughout this article are not approved to diagnose, treat, cure or prevent disease.

THE PAIN YOU HAVE BEEN FEELING CANNOT COMPARE TO THE JOY THAT IS COMING!

The Bible, Romans 8:18

VitaminDLifestyle.com

Vitamin D Lifestyle is Vanessa Raphael's page full of information, interviews and recipes for people interested in or following the Dr. Coimbra Vitamin-D Protocol for autoimmune diseases.

To receive inspiration and valuable tips sign-up to get updated via email at **VitaminDLifestyle.com**

Free 15 Day Introduction Email Course about the Coimbra Protocol

What is the Coimbra Protocol? Is it only about high doses of vitamin D3? Get answers to a "million questions" about Vitamin D3, Calcium restricted diet, Magnesium, Supplements, Exercise and everything that is important to know.

The Coimbra Protocol is known to treat auto immune disorders such as MS, Arthritis Rheumatoid, Lupus, Lyme, and many others.

Take this 15 Day Introduction Email Course and get the knowledge you need to get started. Please register at:
Vitamindlifestyle.com/course

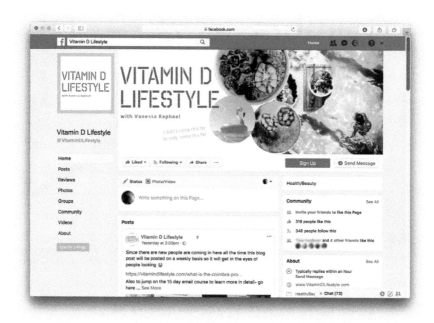

Vitamin D Lifestyle
Facebook Page

Like the page to stay up-to-date via Facebook:

www.facebook.com/VitaminDLifestyle

Vitamin D Lifestyle
Facebook Group

Apply to join the group and join a growing, helpful and positive community. We take great effort in focusing on what's uplifting, inspiring and funny to help us renew and gain strength for our health journey.

www.facebook.com/groups/VitaminDLifestyle

My 60 Days Lifestyle Health Journal
Track your Health, Food, Supplements & Exercise.

A handy journal allowing you to track your health journey in a structured way. By tracking your symptoms, your supplements and your diet all together with exercise you and your doctor are more likely to get a better picture of your health journey over time as a whole.
These journals are available in different designs.
e.g. Ocean Edition and Guy Edition (shown above)

Buy your journal on Amazon.com

Hi,

My name is Tobias and I designed this book with my wife Vanessa Raphael for you.

I'm a recovering perfectionist. - A musician turned graphic designer turned videographer turned video-teacher.

I'm rediscovering the art of focusing more on passion than perfection and offer both video editing courses for beginners, design and animation services as well as uplifting, meditational, electronic soaking music.

You can find my services, courses, blog posts and unusual soaking-meditation-music at **www.tobiasmichel.com**

DON'T GIVE UP ON
THE PERSON YOU ARE
BECOMING.

I HAVEN'T COME THIS FAR, TO ONLY COME THIS FAR!